CONTENTS

6 SEA LEVEL 103

7 CARBON DIOXIDE, METHANE, AND GLOBAL WARMING 123

8 CHLORINATED FLUOROCARBONS (CFCs) AND STRATOSPHERIC OZONE 143

PREFACE

This book aims to address the issues of natural and human induced or accelerated environmental change on the global scale. Concerns about these issues are commonly expressed by questions such as: How does carbon dioxide influence global temperatures? What determines changes in sea level and how do such changes affect the coastal environment? How has the atmospheric composition changed with time? What are the controls of the oceans, the atmosphere, and the physical geography of the land in setting the regional and temporal patterns of climate? How are nature and humans affecting the land? What is the role of natural global catastrophes on life in general and humans in particular?

The answers to each of these questions involve not only the expertise of geologists, atmospheric scientists, and oceanographers, but also that of biologists, astronomers, chemists, physicists, geographers, political scientists, historians, archaeologists, and economists. In order to think globally about environmental change, the provincial boundaries of the classical disciplines must be breached.

This book consists of 11 chapters, each centered around a topic in global change that crosses over the classic disciplinary boundaries. It is by no means comprehensive in its scope. I have included chemical reactions as needed in understanding the processes of global environmental change, and isotopic studies are used as valuable recorders of these changes. This approach requires special effort on the part of the reader. In order to help in this effort, appendixes are added to those chapters requiring a further understanding of the processes alluded to in the chapter. At the end of most of the chapters there are problems intended to help understanding. They are meant as thought problems, rather than as comprehensive tests.

The origins of this book are courses that I have taught at Yale. It all started in two small "college seminars" in one of Yale's residential colleges, Berkeley College. The seminars were entitled "The Earth and Human History" and "The Human View of Earth." These courses satisfied one of the science requirements at Yale and were aimed at nonphysical scientists. From these courses evolved a more formal course, "Global Change," which was targeted at satisfying the science requirement, as well as being one of the entry courses into a major in the Department of Geology and Geophysics. In its first year of offering, the enrollment exceeded 400 students. In each subsequent year, the problems and discussion section activities of the course were gradually expanded and modified. The present book is the product of this progression and is meant to provide a basic outline for a course in global environmental change. It assumes the reader has a knowledge of high school chemistry or physics.

Preliminary lecture notes were distributed to some of the classes as well as to groups of Yale Alumni curious about the environment. This was done at seminars in Chicago, Washington D.C., and at reunions for the classes of 1962 and 1967 in New Haven. The many comments and perceptive questions of these thoughtful alumni helped greatly in shaping this book to be responsive to broader questions than I had at first entertained.

Assistance from a grant from the Noble Foundation helped in improving the presentation to my classes as well as providing them with preliminary notes that led to the present manuscript.

Critical reading of the original manuscript was provided by Robert N. Clayton, The University of Chicago; R. Lawrence Edwards, University of Minnesota; Jeffrey K. Greenberg, Wheaton College; Leon Long, University of Texas; and James C. G. Walker, University of Michigan. I certainly have not satisfied all of their complaints, but I tried. They are blameless for my errors of commission and omission in the manuscript. I thank them for their deep insights into correct science, good writing, and good pedagogy.

Karl K. Turekian

PROLOGUE

Our physical environment changes continuously. The seasons, tides, day and night, and the episodic storms, earthquakes, and volcanic explosions attest to this fact. Our personal environment also changes. The inevitable aging process and the cycle of birth and death are the most fundamental examples of these changes. Revolutions, whether benevolent or violent, migrations, both voluntary and forced, and the formation and destruction of cities and states show that the communal environment also changes. All of these changes can be observed within one person's lifetime, if indeed, the times are "interesting." Poets, who have yearned for constancy (at least in their lovers) and bemoaned change, are often our voices. Yet change is inevitable and humans learn to accommodate or even shape change.

Earth has a great age. It has been around for four and a half billion years. Before humans inhabited Earth, changes were occurring. We did not inherit a planet without a history, but one whose present aspect is linked to the past.

The global vision of our planet has been enhanced by the extensive travels of large numbers of people in modern times, whether for purposes of war or in the pursuit of trade and pleasure. Perhaps the vision of the "big blue marble" brought to us by the cameras of the Apollo astronauts has etched in our minds the grand continuity of Earth through images of large interconnecting oceans and swirling clouds in the atmosphere.

The measurements of scientists tell us that the composition of our atmosphere is changing. The moving air transmits these changes globally, no matter where they are initiated. Fossil-fuel–derived carbon dioxide, for example, although primarily injected into the atmosphere in the northern hemisphere, has been found to be increasing systematically all over the world. Again, it is the poet who gives us our voice. "No man is an island," John Donne wrote over three hundred years ago and, using another metaphor, pronounced, "Send not to ask for whom the bell tolls—it tolls for thee."

Most discussions of global environmental change at the present time have been focusing on "global warming" imputed to be due, in part at least, to the increasing carbon dioxide level in the atmosphere resulting from fossil fuel burning. Serious concern has also arisen over the depletion of stratospheric ozone, so markedly demonstrated in the Antarctic region. But global environmental change has larger dimensions than these human accelerated changes. Mutation is the essence of the history of the planet. Larger changes in atmospheric chemistry have occurred in the past than are seen at present. Swings in sea level are clearly marked in the geological record, and they are much greater than those occurring in the last 100 years. The temperature of Earth has ranged widely on the million-year timescale as well as timescales of centuries or even less. Changes on Earth have been occurring throughout its existence—most of them more dramatic than any we observe today. We especially care about the recent changes, whether natural- or human-accelerated, since we perceive these changes to affect our lives and weal directly. Our understanding of the past will help put these perceptions in a more environmentally sound framework.

We depend on the chroniclers, the storytellers, and the poets to give us a sense of place and purpose. We depend on the chroniclers of the physical environment to describe the anatomy, physiology, and pathologies of our planet. Indeed, our perceptions of the place of humans on Earth is strongly conditioned by our views of the history of Earth, whether we are immediately aware of it or not. Our goal is to consider how this grand view of Earth can affect our thinking about the politics and sociology of global change. We must consider what we can reasonably do to influence or ameliorate global environmental change for the benefit of humans as dwellers and caretakers of Earth, and how we can live with what we cannot change.

1

THE CHANGING PLANET

The campaign of exploration of our solar system by means of spaceship robots with names like *Voyager, Mariner, Magellan,* and *Galileo* has given us a new perspective on the planets. The innermost planet, Mercury, like our own moon, is a pockmarked planet storing a record of the intense meteorite bombardment of the inner solar system more than three and a half billion years ago. The face of Venus was hidden to us until recently by a dense atmosphere of carbon dioxide and clouds of sulfuric acid droplets. When *Magellan's* radar systematically scanned the surface it revealed a volcanic terrain with high volcanoes and smooth plains of lava—evidently with eruptive activity occurring continuously to the present. Mars has a thin atmosphere also composed primarily of carbon dioxide. Mars is a rusty-looking planet with polar ice caps of water and dry ice (frozen carbon dioxide). Both orbiting remote sensors and close-up observations from a robot lander show a terrain of pulverized rock and dust in which additional water, as ice, is probably hidden. The "red" planet, Mars, owes its color to a coating of iron oxide "rust" resulting from the weathering of its volcanically originating rocks. Seasonal transport of the condensed gases in the ice caps provides our only impression of seasons in the innermost solar system aside from that which we experience on our own planet.

Earth is unique. For one thing it is the people on Earth who are discovering the make-up of the solar system and beyond. And people would not exist except for the relatively benign surface conditions on our planet made possible by the presence of liquid water. Yet humans are recent inhabitants of

Earth. For four and a half billion years of its existence Earth has undergone radical changes. The amount and composition of the atmosphere have altered, the continents have formed, the oceans have been emplaced and life evolved. None of the other planets have experienced such radical changes. Indeed, Earth is the markedly changing planet in the solar system. These changes are the consequence of Earth's distance from the sun, the presence of liquid water on Earth's surface, and the initiation and development of life on our planet.

THE ORIGIN OF THE SOLAR SYSTEM AND EARTH

The universe we see through telescopes as galaxies and their component stars appears to be about 10 to 15 billion years old. This age is determined by examining the spectra of galactic light measured through telescopes. The shift of the spectra toward the red, or longer wavelengths, compared to the spectrum from our own Sun is called the "red shift." This shift is greater the more distant the galaxy is from ours, and this observation can be used to determine the rate of movement of galaxies away from each other. This dispersion rate can then be translated into the age when all the components were in one spot, which is inferred to be the age of the universe prior to expansion.

At that time the whole universe was in one tiny spot composed of pure intense energy from which all matter was formed as the universe expanded. Galaxies are the consequent product of this expansion and their primary composition was hydrogen and to a lesser extent helium. Stars are formed, modified, and destroyed continuously in the galaxies. As gas and dust swirl around, clusters of matter, drawn together by gravity, coalesce to form stars. The accumulation of spinning matter could dissipate an embryonic star. Stars, therefore, commonly are formed as binaries—two stars revolving around each other—thus transferring the spin (or more properly the angular momentum) to the binary system, which all but eliminates the spinning of each of the stars on their individual axes.

A solar system is another way to accommodate this spin problem. Virtually all of the mass of the solar system is in the sun while, by far, most of the spin (or more properly, angular momentum) is found in the revolution of the planets roughly in a plane described by Earth's orbit around the sun. The great mass of the planets is in the major or outer planets, especially Jupiter. These outer planets are massive but of low density. They are composed primarily of hydrogen and helium. The inner planets (Mercury, Venus, Earth, and Mars) are all of the density expected for a composition of rock and iron resembling the meteorites often seen to fall on Earth and commonly preserved in museums. The properties of the planets are shown in Table 1–1.

TABLE 1–1 Properties of the Planets

	Sun	Mercury	Venus	Earth	Mars	Jupiter	Saturn	Uranus	Neptune	Pluto
Mass (Earth = 1)	329,000	0.054	0.81	1[a]	0.11	314	94	14.4	17.0	0.05?
Radius (km)	695,000	2439	6050	6370	3400	71,000	57,000	25,800	22,300	2900
Density (g/cm^3)	1.41	5.42	5.25	5.52	3.95	1.33	0.68	1.60	1.65	3?
Albedo		0.06	0.73	0.39	0.26	0.51	0.50	0.66	0.62	–
Effective temperature (°K)	6000	616	235	240	220	105	75	50	40	40
Surface temperature (°K)		616	600	300	230	130	–	–	–	–
Observed gases in atmosphere	H, He O, Fe N, Mg C, Si, etc.	Na	CO_2 H_2O HCl	N_2, O_2 Ar, CO_2 H_2O etc.	CO_2 H_2O	H_2, CH_4 NH_3	H_2, CH_4	H_2, CH_4	–	–
Distance from the sun (A.U.)[b]		0.39	0.72	1	1.52	5.2	9.5	19.2	30.1	

[a]The mass of Earth is 5.976×10^{27}g.

[b]A.U. = "Astronomic unit"—the mean distance of the earth from the sun (149.6×10^6 km).

The formation of the solar system, then, is the consequence of concentrating galactic gas and dust into a spinning mass from which the sun and planets have been formed by gravitational accretion. The planets have been formed along the plane of the sun's rotation and carry most of the spin (more properly, the angular momentum) of the solar system. This partitioning of mass and spin between the sun and its planets makes for a stable system. The sun does not obliterate itself by spinning too fast since the planets take up the spin requirement of the system by revolving around it.

Between Mars and Jupiter lies a band of very small planetary bodies called asteroids that also revolve around the sun. These objects have eccentric orbits and occasionally strike Earth and are recovered as meteorites. These meteorites provide us with information about how planetary material may have looked early in the history of the solar system. The extremely cold environment of the outermost part of the solar system is the source of the comets, such as Halley's comet. Comets are composed of rocky material, organic compounds, and ice. Each comet follows its own highly eccentric orbit around the sun.

Occasionally large comets or asteroids are intercepted by a planet and the result is a highly energetic collision. The collision of comet Shoemaker-Levy 9 with Jupiter in July 1994 provided astronomers with a detailed picture of such an event. A recent example of such a collision with Earth is the comet or meteorite that struck Siberia in 1908 in the region of Tunguska. The Tunguska event knocked down trees within a thousand square miles and sent shock waves and debris around the world. The extraterrestial object struck in one of the most unpopulated regions of the world and no one was killed or injured. If it had hit a population center, the effects would have been much greater than those of the atomic bombs dropped at Hiroshima and Nagasaki combined!

Evidence for collisions of meteorites and comets with the planets is clear not only from the craters on Earth but also from the display of highly cratered surfaces on Mercury and our own moon. Indeed the moon itself may have been the direct consequence of a super collision of a Mars-sized body with primitive Earth. Earth is different from the other inner planets in that it is the only planet with one very large moon, and this collision may be the reason. Venus and Mercury have no moons and Mars has two very small ones.

THE INTERIOR OF EARTH

The structure of Earth is inferred from the study of earthquake waves; the discipline called *seismology*. The composition of Earth's interior is inferred from the rocks we see at the surface, from the study of meteorites, and through laboratory experiments.

When an earthquake occurs, energy waves resembling sound waves are transmitted away from the site, or *focus,* of the earthquake. (The place on Earth's surface directly above the focus is called the *epicenter.*) Lines from the focus to the wave front are known as rays. Generally, with increasing depth, because of pressure-dependent changes in the transmissive properties of the interior, the velocity of the waves increases. The ray is bent as it passes progressively through material in which the velocity of sound increases with increasing depth. This bending is called *refraction* and results in arcuate paths which reach the surface of Earth at different points depending on the trajectory of the ray. *Seismographs,* deployed around Earth's surface, will record the first arrival of earthquake waves at different times depending on their distances from the focus. However, between 105° and 141° along the arc of a great circle drawn through the epicenter, these first strong impulse earthquake waves are not received. This absence of an expected signal suggests that a phase boundary with a sharp decrease in the sound velocity of the medium has been encountered by the wave at some depth along the path. This boundary, or *discontinuity,* is inferred to be the demarcation of the iron-nickel *core,* below, and the *mantle,* above, composed predominantly of magnesium, iron, calcium, aluminum, silicon, and oxygen. The outer layer of the core is molten while the inner core is solid, based on the study of different types of seismic waves. The inferred structure of Earth is shown in Figure 1–1. The outermost part of Earth is called the *crust* but it is so thin that it does not show up in a figure drawn to scale. The boundary between the crust and the mantle is also a

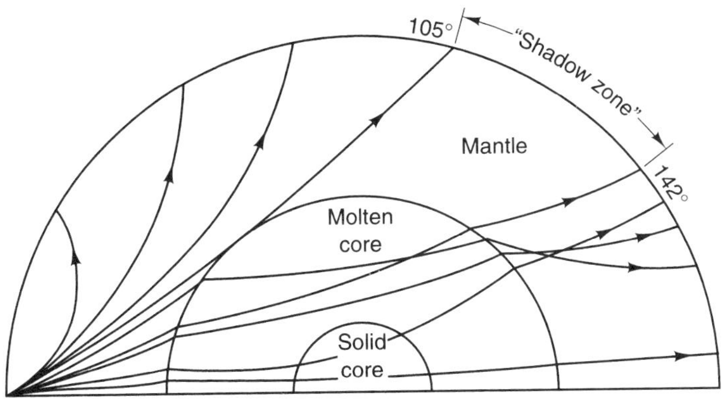

FIGURE 1–1 The interior structure of Earth inferred from seismic waves (after K. E. Bullen). The density of Earth is about 5.5 g cm^{-3}. As the silicate rock of the kind expected in the mantle is about 3.2 g cm^{-3}, we infer that the core of Earth is composed of iron (with some nickel). This inference is compatible with the abundance of iron meteorites. The outer core is inferred to be molten iron (nickel) based on the fact that seismic waves requiring a solid medium are not transmitted through it.

sharp discontinuity, based primarily on compositional differences between the two units. The crust-mantle boundary, called the *Mohorovičić discontinuity,* is deeper under mountain roots, in particular, and under continents, generally (about 40 km), and is shallower under the deep ocean basins (about 5 km).

The heat reaching the surface of our planet from the interior, at the present time, comes partially from the initial gravitational heat produced during Earth's formation—that is, the accumulation of small fragments of meteorite-like materials called planetesimals and the moon-forming collision. However, primarily the heat is produced by natural radioactivity.

Natural radioactivity in Earth is supplied mainly by the elements uranium, thorium, and potassium. A discussion of the details of radioactivity is deferred to the next chapter. The important consequence of radioactivity for the heating of Earth is that as nuclear particles are emitted from the radioactive atoms and the nuclei adjust to the changes resulting from this loss, energy is also generated and given off to the surrounding Earth material. This tends to warm up the interior of Earth. As it warms up, heat escapes from the interior. We can clearly see this escape in the form of volcanoes and hot springs but there is also heat flow through rocks. As time goes by the radioactive heat source diminishes and the temperature of Earth's interior tends to decrease in response to the lower heat production. Over the billions of years of Earth's history there has been a slow decrease in the production of heat from radioactivity inside the planet. Because of this decrease the processes we see at the surface, driven by the escape of Earth's internal heat, are also decreasing in intensity. The loss of this heat from Earth's interior is principally effected not by conduction, as occurs in metals, or radiation, as sensed through a pane of glass, but by the convection of the hot interior, as with boiling water.

Convection occurs by the movement of deep, hot mantle toward the surface of the planet. Cooling at the surface occurs by conduction, radiation, and volcanic action. The cooled upper mantle and mantle-derived rocks are then returned to depth to complete the convective cycle. It is this process that is responsible for the formation of mountains and ocean basins, as we shall see at the end of this chapter.

EARTH AS A MAGNET

Just as convection occurs in the mantle so also does it occur in the outer molten part of the iron-nickel core. The energy for core convection comes from crystallization of the molten iron-nickel, chemical reactions at the core-mantle boundary, and interactions with the magnetic field of the sun. On a rotating planet such as Earth a molten core acts like a dynamo, and a magnetic field develops. In a dynamo the flow of electrical current through coiled wires creates a magnetic field. The flow of an electric conductor, molten metal, in a rotating planet simulates this effect. The other inner or terrestrial planets do not have significant magnetic fields because they either lack molten iron-nickel cores, as in the case of Mars, or are not rotating rapidly enough, because of tidal restraints of the sun, to effect a dynamo as in the case of Venus. (Mercury is too small and too close to the sun to meet either requirement.)

In a so-called "bar magnet"—that is, a bar of iron that has been magnetized—the ends of the bar are designated "north" and "south," alluding to the fact that Earth, at the present time, behaves like an iron bar magnet with one magnetic "pole" approximately at the north geographic pole and the other at approximately the south geographic pole. Such a configuration is called a dipole magnet. Small magnetized iron particles will align themselves in the magnetic field of such a dipole magnet. The alignment of the little magnets describes an array which is interpreted as being the response to lines of force connecting north and south poles of the dominant magnet. These lines of forcc exist on Earth as well as around a bar magnet and, of course, the pattern provides the basis of the magnetic compass. At present, the south magnetic pole is located around the north geographic pole. That is, the north magnetic poles of common compasses point north as they align themselves along Earth's magnetic lines of force.

Although Earth's magnetic field is a dipole, the polarity of the field need not remain constant in time because, unlike a bar magnet, the polarity is the consequence of a conducting fluid in motion, the basis of the dynamo that makes the magnetic field. Earth's magnetic field intensity can vary over time on a random basis. When the field is so low as to be virtually absent, the reformation of the magnetic field can result in Earth having the same polarity as before the diminution of the field or the opposite polarity. That is, Earth's field can be "normal" as it is today where the north magnetic pole is at the south geographic pole, or "reversed" where the north magnetic pole is at the north geographic pole (Fig. 1–2).

The time record of these switches in magnetic polarity has been determined precisely, at least for the past 5 million years, using dating methods based on natural radioactivity, as described in the next chapter. As lava flows erupt on Earth, magnetic minerals in the solidified rock orient themselves in Earth's magnetic field much like a compass. The orientation is fixed in the rock, however, and that orientation will not change thereafter, no matter how Earth's field changes. The radioactive dating of these flows, whose geographic orientations are known, provides a record of Earth's magnetic polarity over time (Fig. 1–3).

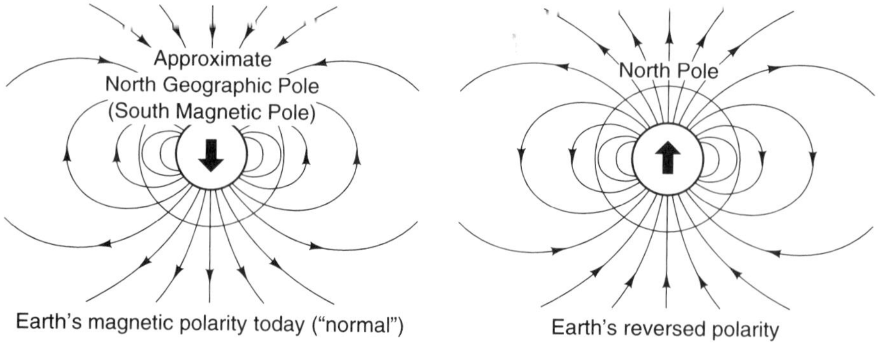

FIGURE 1–2 The Earth as a magnet. The north magnetic pole of Earth at the present time is found in the vicinity of the south geographic pole. That is why the north poles of magnets point north, following the lines of force of Earth's magnet. The reversed polarity (relative to the present) occurs when the north magnetic pole and the north geographic pole are coincident. The "lines of force" describe the way free-swinging compasses would point.

THE SURFACE FEATURES OF EARTH

The features of Earth's surface are determined by responses to two energy sources: the interior heat of the planet and the heat from the sun. About 5400 times more heat per unit area comes to Earth's surface from the sun than from Earth's interior (sun = 3.4×10^{-2} watts cm^{-2}; Earth's interior = 6.3×10^{-6} watts cm^{-2}). The sun's energy is used mainly to heat air, water, rocks, and soil at Earth's surface and to maintain most life. The energy from the interior of Earth is responsible for making continents, ocean basins, mountains, and volcanoes. The features of Earth's surface derive from the consequences of the two energy sources. One creates mountains, for example, and the other is responsible for eroding them.

To a visitor from another planet the most obvious features of Earth's surface would be oceans and continents (Fig. 1–4). Then, with better visual resolution the visitor would notice the presence of ice caps and islands. On detailed aerial, satellite, and land-based mapping using a variety of sensors, the visitor would identify mountain ranges, volcanoes, high plateaus, plains, deserts, and river systems. Clouds, of course, would obscure vision at various times and in various places. With special submarine sensors the visitor would discover that the wavy ocean surface hides a complex topography of ridges, submarine volcanoes, and deep trenches as well as plains and deltas. Of course, humans have described these features already in their "mission to planet Earth."

FIGURE 1–3 The changes in magnetic polarity of Earth over the past 5 million years as inferred from dated and oriented lava flows. Normal polarity is marked *N;* reversed polarity is marked *R.* The boundary between the present normal polarity and the reversed polarity ending at 780,000 years ago is called the Brunhes-Matuyama boundary. (Constructed from the compilation of S. C. Cande and D. V. Kent, 1995, *J. Geophys. Res.,* v. 100, p. 6093.)

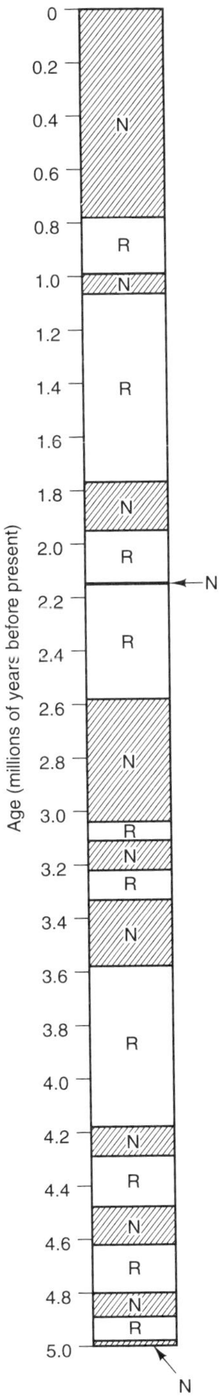

FIGURE 1–4 Major features of Earth's surface and ocean bottom. (Originally created by B. C. Heezen and M. Tharp and published by the American Geographical Society on behalf of the U.S. Navy.)

The distributions of the features just described are not haphazard but are the consequences of the action of the energy from the interior and the energy from the sun shaping the planet's surface. The sun causes water to evaporate from the oceans. The differential heating of the planet from the pole to the equator causes the heat-and-moisture–laden air from the equator to move toward the poles. Imposed on this flow is the seasonal cycle. As

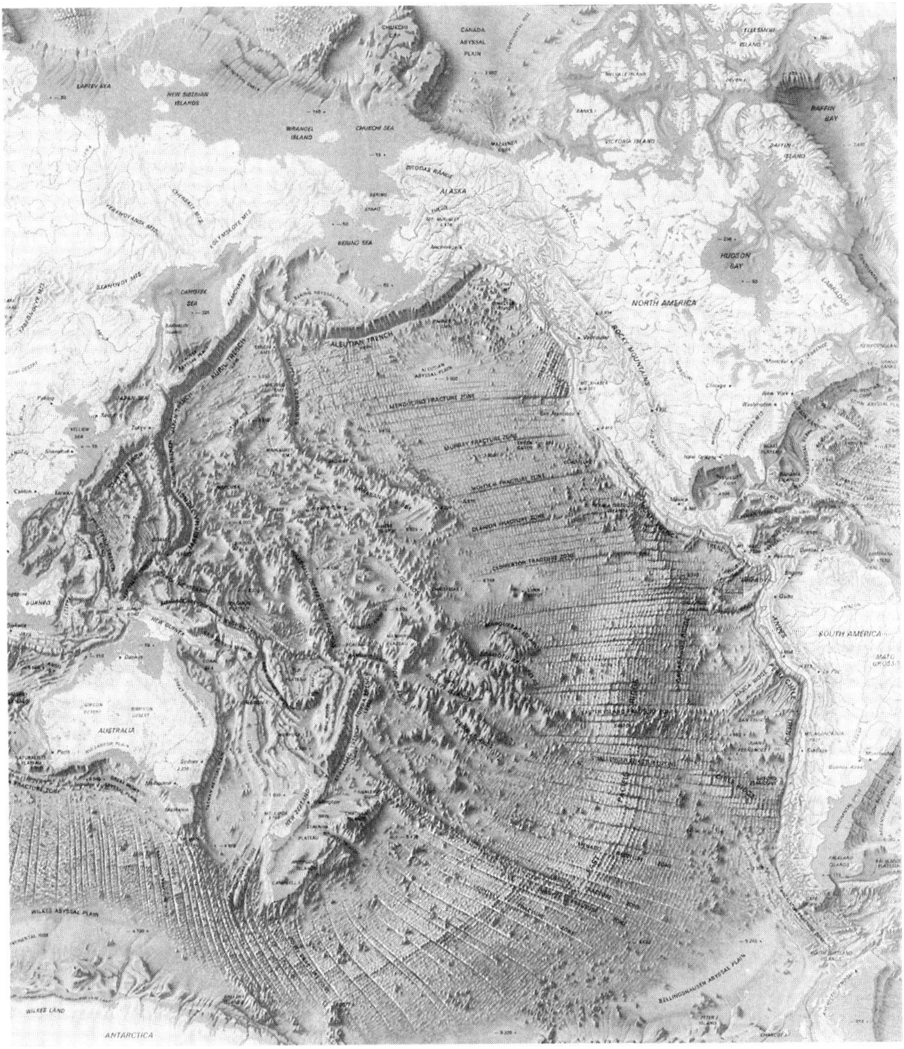

moisture-laden air is lifted over highlands or where convective storms occur, water precipitates and vegetation flourishes, causing the weathering and erosion of the land. The streams drain away the water to the oceans with loads of sediment and dissolved chemicals. Meanwhile, the mountains are regenerated or new mountains form in response to the flux of energy from the interior of the planet.

PLATE TECTONICS

All our knowledge of earthquakes, the distribution of continents, deep-sea topography, and the magnetic record in stratified rocks and the ocean floor points to a highly mobile planetary surface. The driving force is convection in the mantle produced by heating in Earth's interior.

In the middle of the nineteenth century it was realized that the continents on either side of the Atlantic Ocean seemed to fit like a jigsaw puzzle—if you moved them across the Atlantic. In particular, Africa and South America make a nice fit. From the observation and evidence that rocks from the two distant continents share similar fossils, sediment types, and age it was inferred early in the twentieth century that indeed the continents of the Old and New Worlds were once joined. The idea that the placement of the present-day continents was the result of the break-up and separation of a much larger continental mass came to be called "continental drift"—that is, the continents seemed to have "drifted" across the face of Earth much as split ice floes might do in the polar oceans. As geophysicists could not conceive of how hard rocks could float across other rocks on such grand scales, the idea was heatedly debated, with some paleontologists and geologists on the side favoring continental drift, and most other geologists and geophysicists in opposition. Yet the geophysicists and oceanographers, with their questioning attitude, were to provide the rationale for the movements occurring in the outer shell of Earth. The evidence came from a variety of observations.

The major ridge systems in the ocean basin form a series of connected, topographically high areas present in all the oceans (see Fig. 1–4). Ridges are between 1000 and 4000 km wide with a relief of 2 to 4 km above the ocean floor. The crests of the ridges everywhere are about 2.5 km below the ocean surface. The term "mid-ocean ridge" has been used for the submarine mountain system after the most prominent example, the Mid-Atlantic Ridge. Along the axes of the ridge systems are troughs. These have been called rift valleys, based on similar features seen on land such as the valleys in East Africa associated, for example, with Lake Tanganyika. These rift valleys are deeper in the Atlantic relative to the crests than in the other oceans. Heat flow from Earth's interior at the axes of the ridges is higher than anywhere else in the deep ocean basins and indicates that they are sites of the major heat loss from Earth as a result of mantle convection and magma (that is, molten rock) generation and its release as lava flows.

We noted above that when a lava flow begins to crystallize, the magnetic minerals formed in the process are oriented according to the magnetic polarity at the time of emplacement. The intensity of the magnetic field measured by a magnetometer is determined primarily by Earth's large dipole field, but locally it is modified by the presence of magnets with their own fields that may lie close to the magnetometer. A large mass of iron or a magnetized rock locally will influence the intensity of the magnetic field. If a magnetized body is aligned in its polar orientation with the magnetic field of Earth, the magnetic field intensity measured by a magnetometer is increased. If, however, a magnetized body is present with the polarity in the opposite sense relative to Earth's dipole field, the magnetic field intensity is decreased. The increases or decreases of magnetic field intensity beyond the expected field intensity for Earth's present dipole field at any location are called "anomalies"—a *positive* anomaly means the magnets in the rocks are reinforcing today's magnetic field and a *negative* anomaly means the polarity of the magnets in the rocks is reversed relative to today's field and therefore, locally, the magnets are subtracting from Earth's normal magnetic field intensity. A sensitive magnetometer towed by a ship or airplane is able to sense the variations in magnetic intensity anomalies along the track of the vessel or aircraft.

By this procedure, a map of magnetic anomalies has been made for the oceans (Fig. 1–5). The anomaly patterns are symmetrical around the ocean ridge systems. The simplest explanation for this remarkable pattern is that the ridges are spreading apart accompanied by the emplacement of volcanic rocks. This divergence (spreading) is occurring in response to the convecting mantle, and the volcanic rocks record the magnetic polarity at the time of emplacement. As the anomaly pattern closest to the axis of the ridge resembles the magnetic reversal variation history as discussed (Fig. 1–3), this provides us with a chronology of ocean floor spreading for the past 5 million years (the present limit of precise enough radioactive dating of volcanic sequences for this purpose). The rates of spreading for each side of the ridge axis inferred from these data are about 1 cm per year in the Atlantic and about 5 cm per year in the Pacific. By assuming that the spreading rate in each ocean has remained reasonably constant and comparing the anomaly pattern proceeding away from the ridge axis with older, dated magnetic reversal records on land, we can assign an age to each location on the ocean floor since that part of the floor was formed at a ridge crest. Deep-sea drilling has recovered sediments that contain fossils compatible with these assigned ages, thereby supporting the hypothesis of ocean floor spreading. The oldest determined age on the ocean floor, by inference from the magnetic anomaly map, is about 200 million years. The fossil evidence confirms this finding. Obviously, if Earth is much older than 200 million years, the ocean floor is being renewed continuously. Evidence in the next chapter argues for the age of Earth to be several billion years.

The study of earthquakes provides another clue to the processes acting in the outer spheres of Earth. The distribution of earthquakes, geographically and with depth, has been catalogued now for many years, and a clear pattern emerges (Fig. 1–6). The major ocean ridges have more earthquakes

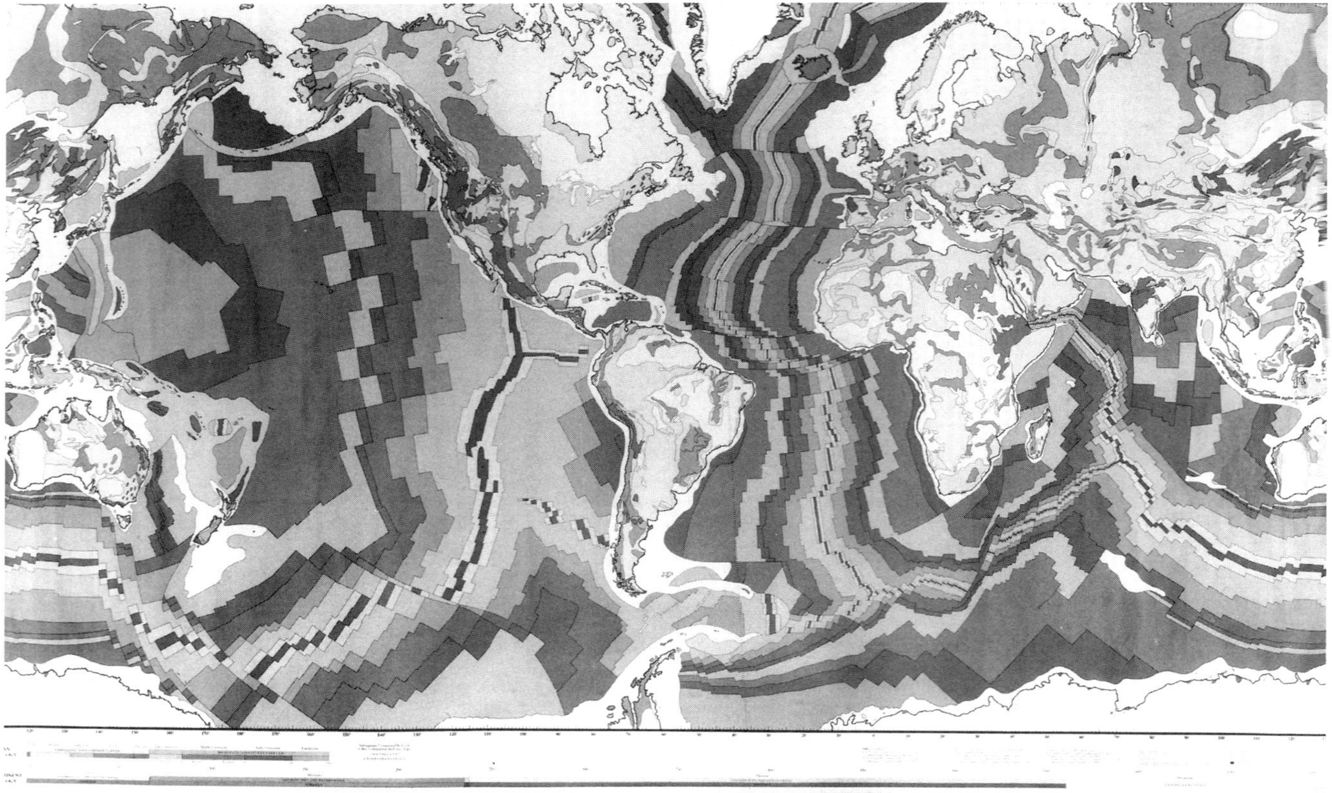

FIGURE 1–5 A geologic map of the oceans (age distribution of oceanic crust) based on magnetic anomaly patterns. (Compiled by R. L. Larson, W. C. Pitman III et al., 1985, W. H. Freeman and Company, Inc. Copyright R. L. Larson and W. C. Pitman III; used with permission.)

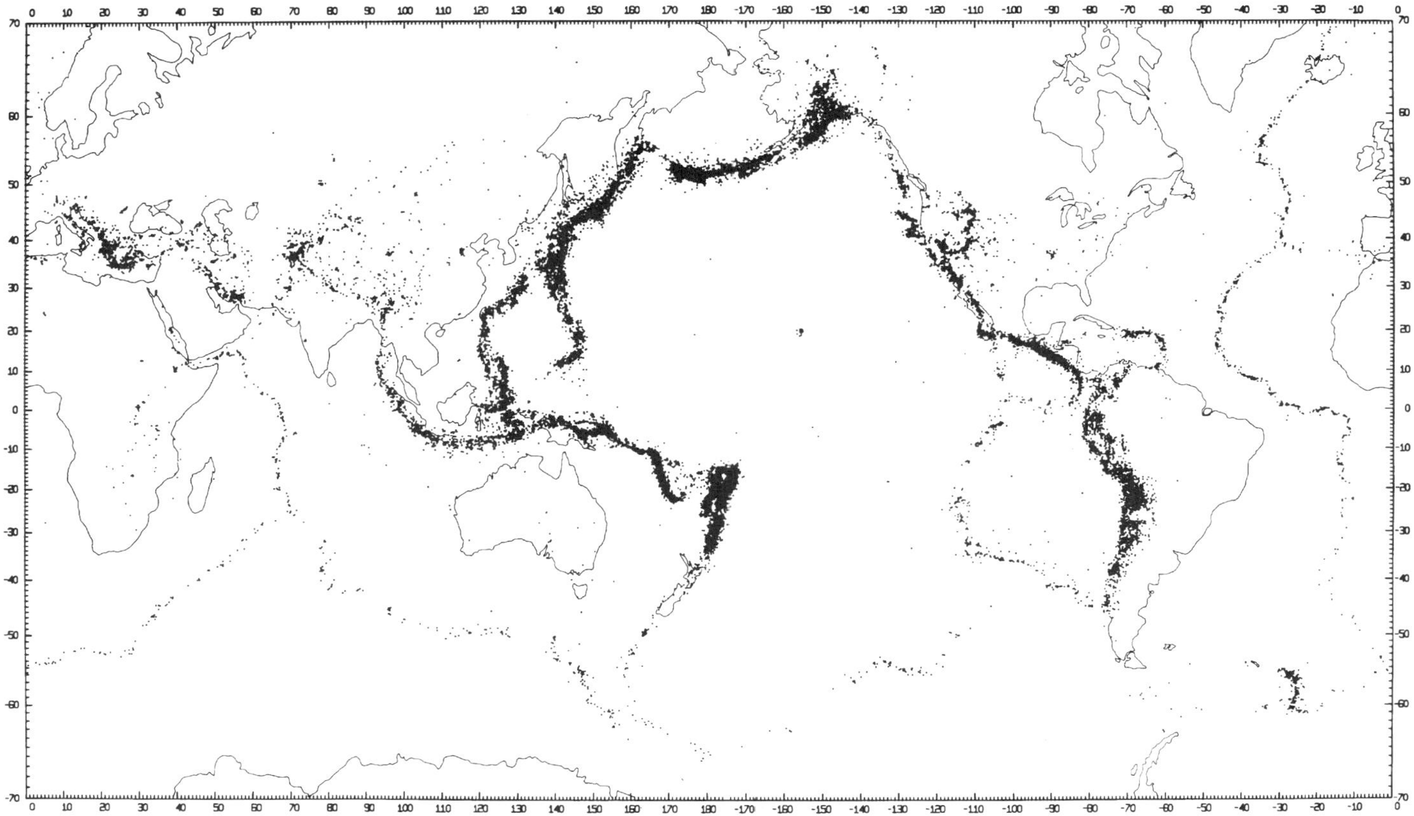

FIGURE 1–6 Seismicity of Earth as recorded between 1961 and 1967 with foci from 0 to 700 kilometers. (From NOAA data compiled by M. Barazangi and J. Dorman, 1969, *Bull. Seism. Soc. Am.,* v. 59, p. 369.)

than the rest of the ocean basin except for those ocean margins where there are deep trenches. The earthquakes along the ridges have shallow foci (about 50 km). Along trenches and associated island arcs or coastal mountains, the earthquakes have foci ranging from the surface down to depths of as much as 700 km. The foci are not haphazardly distributed but along each trench-island arc or coastal mountain region their loci describe a plane generally slanting away from the oceanic side toward the arc or mountain side. The angles between Earth's surface and the plane made by the loci of earthquake foci range around 45° (Fig. 1–7). This configuration implies energy release along the plane and is interpreted to mean that the oceanic upper mantle and associated volcanic rocks are transported under a continental margin or under another oceanic section of upper mantle and associated volcanic rocks.

These three lines of evidence, as well as others, have led to the theory of "plate tectonics." This theory differs from the older continental drift theory in that the operational unit is now a "plate" with a thickness of about 150 km (the

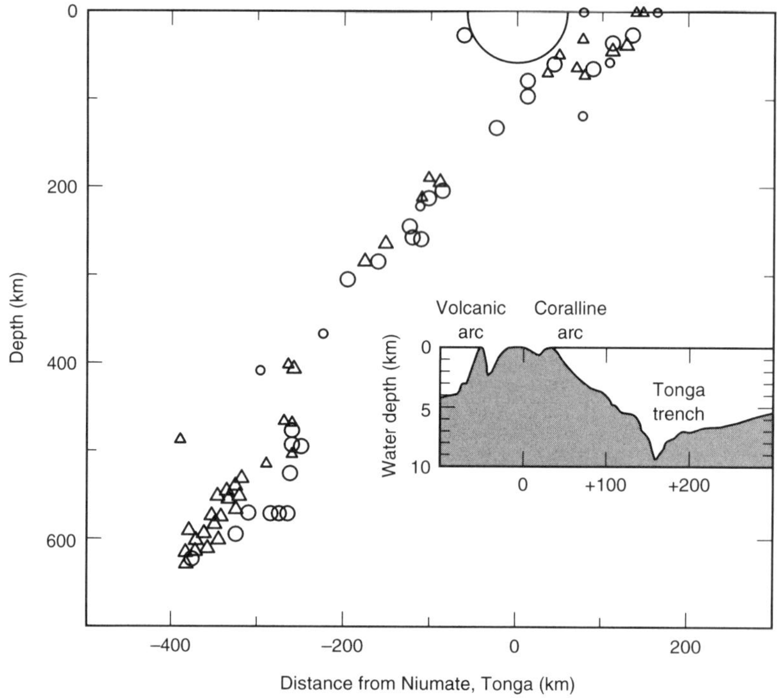

FIGURE 1–7 The earthquake foci along the Tonga-Kermadec trench. (From B. Isacks, J. Oliver, and L. R. Sykes, 1968, *J. Geophys. Res.*, v. 73, p. 5855. Copyright by the American Geophysical Union.)

lithosphere) rather than merely the continental crust with a thickness of about 40 km. It is the plates that are in motion. Plates can carry both continents and ocean basins, and their divergences and convergences result in the creation and destruction of crust at the edges, respectively.

Earth's surface is divided into seven major plates and several other smaller plates (Fig. 1–8). Where plates diverge new oceanic crust is formed and where they converge crust is destroyed by transfer back into the mantle (Fig. 1–9). As the result of mantle convection, the plates are ever in motion relative to each other. The oceanic side of a plate can converge with another plate's oceanic side to produce islands such as the Aleutians or Japan. The convergence results in the major deep-focus earthquakes and the release of intensive explosive volcanism. A similar pattern of deep-focus earthquakes and volcanic chains is present at the convergence of an oceanic plate and the continental margin of another plate. This feature is seen in the Andes and the Cascades. Where a continental edge of a plate converges with another continental edge large mountains and plateaus are formed. For example, the Himalayas and the Tibetan Plateau are the result of the collision of India with Asia, which began about 50 million years ago. Ancient collisions of this sort are seen in the geological record as sites of the melting and mobilization of material formed from continental rocks. The result is a zone of granite intrusions and intensely altered rocks. These zones of convergence, whether occurring now or inferred to have occurred in the past by the study of ancient terrains, are called *suture zones* and show that plates containing continents can agglomerate.

About 250 million years ago a megacontinent, Pangaea, was formed by accretion involving plate convergence activity (Fig. 1–10). Pangaea persisted for about 50 million years before it started breaking up by rifting and then drifting. Evidence for rifting is seen in the ancient rift valleys preserved in the eastern United States along the Connecticut River and throughout New Jersey and Pennsylvania. The great African rift valleys of the present time, including Lake Tanganyika and Lake Kivu, are examples of contemporary "rifting" that have not yet led to "drifting." The study of ancient rocks on the continents shows that the process of agglomeration of the continents into one or a few large masses followed by break-up occurs on about a 400-million-year time scale.

Plate tectonics provides the basis of the fundamental framework for understanding global change. The formation of massive highlands, new waterways of the ocean, and the location of continental masses significantly control the global environment. Monsoons, deserts, ice caps, sea-level changes—all ultimately are driven by the plate tectonic "stage setting" on which the sun then operates to transfer water and heat around the globe.

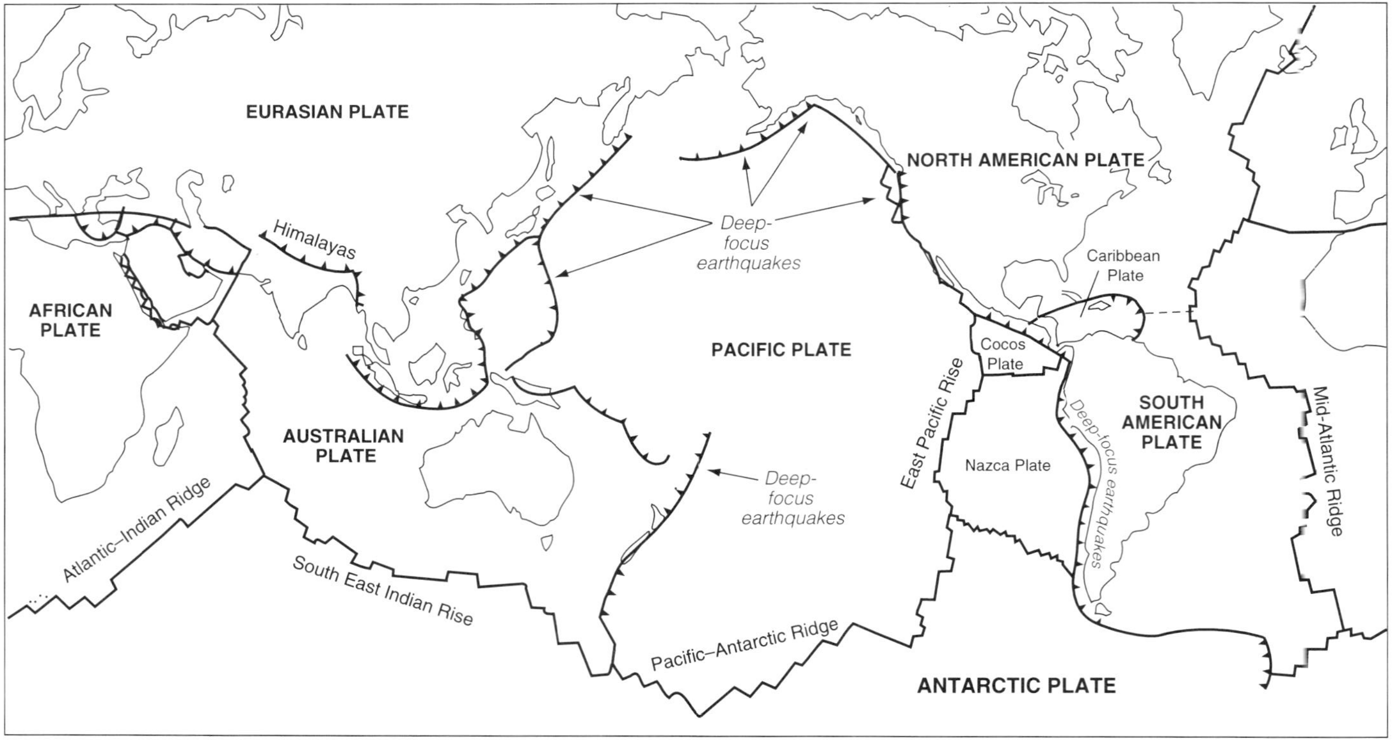

FIGURE 1–8 The division of the Earth into "plates." (After J. D. Dewey; based on earlier constructions by F. Vine and D. Matthews, 1972, *Sci. Am.*, v. 226:16, p. 56.)

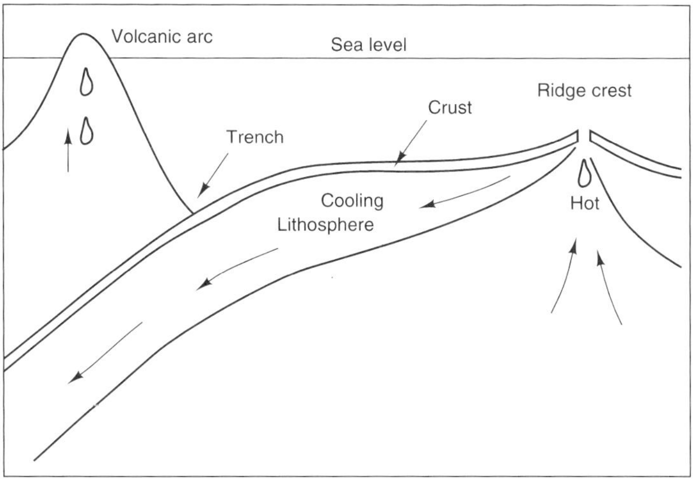

FIGURE 1–9 A representation of the divergent and convergent plate boundaries. Sea floor is generated at the mid-ocean ridges and spreads. Where the oceanic plate encounters another plate, subduction of the plate back into the mantle occurs.

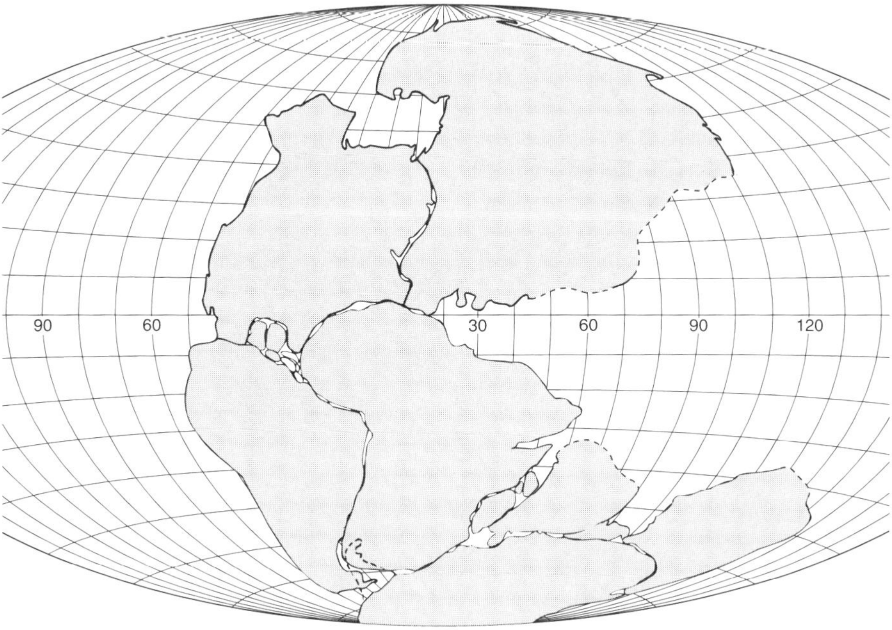

FIGURE 1–10 The megacontinent of Pangaea formed by the accretion of continental "pieces" about 250 million years ago. The breaking apart of Pangaea started 50 million years after it was formed along the lines demarking the present continents. (Modified after R. Dietz and R. Holdren and later reconstructions.)

PROBLEM:

A. Hoover Dam on the Colorado River, near Las Vegas, Nevada, was built in 1936. The dam created Lake Mead. The engineers who designed the dam had to determine how long it would take to silt up Lake Mead completely as the result of trapping of the sediment carried by the Colorado River. These are the data they probably worked with:

- Reservoir capacity = $35,154 \times 10^6$ cubic meters
- Water flow rate of Colorado River = 21×10^{12} liters per year
- Sediment concentration of Colorado River = 13.9 grams per liter
- Density of sediment = 2 grams per cubic centimeter
  = 2×10^6 grams per cubic meter

How long will it take for Lake Mead to be completely filled with sediment?

B. The average height above sea level of all the continents is 800 meters and the average rate of lowering (or "denudation") by erosion (as determined by the type of measurements shown in the first question) is 6 centimeters per thousand years. If this rate of denudation remains the same even as the land is lowered by erosion and if no new mountains are formed, how long will it take to bring all the continents from 800 meters to sea level by erosion?

2

CHRONOLOGY

The measure of time is a fundamental requirement for documenting environmental changes in Earth. A precise chronology allows us to understand the rates and patterns of changes in climate, the pace of planetary history, and the rates of human-induced environmental changes.

Since humans invented writing and began recording events within a chronological context about 5000 years ago, we have some measure of the changes they observed locally. The identification of natural catastrophic events, as well as wars, and what we now regard as architectural triumphs, are recorded in the annals of those civilizations that had developed a strong sense of written history. The events recorded may have different degrees of adherence to the actual facts, yet there remain the records of significant environmental changes such as droughts and floods.

Not all societies left such records over the past 5000 years and there are no written records at all before that time. A global chronology of the past 5000 years requires a way of correlating events in the nonliterate societies with those in the literate societies. If items of exchange between these two types of societies are found in archaeological excavations, we can begin to arrive at the local environmental history in the context of broader changes.

ENVIRONMENTAL RECORDERS WITH BUILT-IN CHRONOMETERS

If we had a chronometer independent of the nature of the human society's ability to write, we would have a way of assessing local environmental changes as well as the ability to correlate events worldwide. There are several natural recorders that provide us with a chronology of environmental change. These include trees, ice caps, corals, and sediments because they grow or accumulate mass with time. If an annual seasonal pattern is recorded during the growth or accumulation process, it is possible to count back in one of these types of environmental recorders to get a precisely timed sequence of changes in the environment.

In climates subject to seasonal changes in sunlight duration, temperature, and water availability, vegetation commonly shows seasonal patterns. Most trees growing in temperate climates record these seasonal changes in their production of rings. By cutting a section from the trunk or making a boring, rings can be counted (Fig. 2–1). By this method some trees, such as the Giant Sequoia, have been shown to be over 2000 years old. As no two years are exactly the same climatologically, the sequences of annual rings are

FIGURE 2–1 A cross section of the trunk of a Douglas fir shows the method of dating tree rings *(dendrochronology)*. The annual variability of ring widths in this species provides a record of climate change during the life of the tree. (Photograph courtesy of the Laboratory of Tree-Ring Research, the University of Arizona.)

characteristically thin or thick. The pattern in the the sequence of rings can be used to extend the record to dead tree trunks that remain strewn on the landscape or are preserved in bogs. By splicing the record from many trees, both living and dead, in a region, researchers have been able to extend the tree ring chronology back as far as 7000 years. In addition to the changes in climatic conditions from year to year recorded in the thickness of the tree rings, the chemistry of the tree ring itself contains information on changes in temperature, precipitation, and even the intensity of cosmic rays over time.

Large accumulations of snowfall at high elevations and in the polar regions record seasonal changes in precipitation shown by the thickness of seasonal snow layers. Even after compaction and flow of ice as glaciers, these layers can be counted down from the surface in the same fashion that tree rings are counted. Such ice records of the Andes (Fig. 2–2) and the Tibetan Plateau provide a datable record of local environmental conditions seen in the changes in annual accumulation as well as chemical changes. For example, the Andean icefield shows changes in thickness of the annual snow layers which are related to changes in the ocean surface circulation of the southern Pacific Ocean. The changes in ocean and atmospheric circulation have affected the economy of modern Peru. Archaeological evidence shows that times of drought or torrential rains influenced the architecture and the history of the ancient Incas and their neighbors.

Corals growing in warm tropical and subtropical oceans show seasonal growth patterns (Fig. 2–3) which record variations in local marine productivity resulting from changes in ocean circulation. The corals also record the chemical changes due to circulation as well as contemporary pollutant loading. The banding in corals can be used to count back several hundred years. Longer continuous records are virtually impossible to obtain because corals, on death, are either destroyed with time or become the substrates for totally new coral growth if they are not dissolved or transported by ocean waves.

Sediments deposited in water that is poorly oxygenated, such as marginal marine basins like those off southern California and Mexico, provide a record of seasonal changes in biological productivity. The virtual absence of oxygen in the bottom waters does not allow for the survival of most organisms other than bacteria, and this absence of active movement retards the mixing of the sediment so that annual patterns of sedimentation are preserved. Counting the annual sediment layers (commonly called *varves*) from the top of the sediment pile downward gives a measure of time. The thickness and composition of the layers provide information on locally changing conditions due to climate shifts, global ocean circulation changes, and human-induced perturbations. These changes are seen in the amounts of organic matter preserved, the concentration of detrital sediments of various

FIGURE 2–2 Quelccaya ice cap is located in the southern Peruvian Andes at an elevation of 5670 meters. This 50-meter ice cliff at the margin of the ice cap, photographed in 1983, has disappeared as of August 1995 as the result of increasing temperature (discussed in Chapter 6). This ice cap has annual layers (about 0.75 meters each) dating back 1500 years. (Photograph courtesy of Lonnie G. Thompson, Department of Geological Science and Byrd Polar Research Center of The Ohio State University.)

FIGURE 2–3 Photograph of 200-year-old Bermuda coral showing annual bands which provide information on changing ocean conditions. (Photograph courtesy of Richard E. Dodge.)

origins, and the accumulation of diagnostic human contaminants such as beer container caps and other artifacts of the past.

All of these detectors—trees, ice, corals, sediments—combine to give a picture of the changing environment over the past approximately 10,000 years. The extension of the chronometry further back in time by simple counting of from present to back layers, becomes more and more difficult because the chance of survival of the detectors in an unaltered form becomes lower and lower with time. Often we are given fragments of the evidence of the recorders with no continuity to the present. We must turn to other techniques of chronometry if we are to encompass the entire environmental history of Earth.

DETERMINING THE AGE OF EARTH BASED ON EXTRAPOLATIONS FROM THE PRESENT

If we imagine Earth to have a history of about 10,000 years then the detectors described above would be sufficient for deciphering an environmental history of the planet. If the age of Earth is greater, as implied in the previous chapter, then we must obtain a way of calibrating the time dimension with accuracy. To do this we must first settle the question of the age of Earth. During the nineteenth century a serious quest for determining the age of

Earth was begun. Until the beginning of the nineteenth century, the possibility of a young Earth seemed compatible with the record in the Bible, which yielded an age of Earth of about 6000 years. Without an independent assessment of age the only choice was either to accept an age set from religious or historical documents or ignore the need for knowing the age of Earth by assuming steady-state, continuously operating processes. James Hutton, commonly considered the "father" of modern geology, espoused this latter view of Earth in his statement that he "saw no vestige of a beginning, no prospect for an end."

Charles Darwin's *Origin of Species,* published in 1857, implied that a long period of time was required for natural selection to yield the present array of life. This theory and the study of the fossil record changed the way time scales were viewed. These views repudiated both the concept of steady state and a short history of Earth. The evidence showed that there was a progression in life forms with time and, clearly, this required a great deal more than six days some 6000 years ago if Darwinian evolution were responsible. Indeed, this view "saw" vestiges of a beginning and a progression over time. Both facts were compelling arguments for determining the age of Earth.

The methods for determining the age of Earth at the end of the nineteenth century were based on three physical observations of that time: (1) the release of heat from Earth; (2) the rate of supply of sediments by rivers to the oceans and the mass of total sediments accumulated on Earth; and (3) the rate of supply of dissolved sodium by rivers and the saltiness of the sea.

The increasing temperature with depth, observed in deep mines, meant that heat was escaping from Earth's interior. If one assumed that Earth, when it formed, was a molten globe of rock then the measurement of the heat escape rate and the premise that Earth is now solid would allow the determination of the length of time it took for Earth to cool to its present state. Lord Kelvin (after whom the absolute temperature scale is named) made the calculation and concluded that it would take Earth 80 million years to cool to its present state. The discovery of radioactivity at the end of the nineteenth century indicated that heat loss is probably determined by heat production (see the discussion in Chapter 1), therefore no simple measure of time can be obtained by measuring the heat escaping at the present time.

The mass of sediments and sedimentary rocks of all geologic systems throughout the world, when divided by the mass per unit time of sediments delivered by the streams of the world, yields an age of about 120 million years (Table 2–1). This calculation does not allow for recycling by a history of mountain uplift and erosion as the result of plate tectonics.

At the turn of the century John Joly, an Irish scientist, argued that if the oceans started out as a gigantic freshwater lake, the present-day rate of supply

TABLE 2–1 Calculations of the "Age of Earth" Using Sediment and Salt Budgets

1. Duration of Continental Erosion	
Total Mass of Sediments and Sedimentary Rocks	2.4×10^{24} grams
Average Sediment Concentration of Rivers	0.400 grams per liter
Worldwide Total River Flow	3.6×10^{16} liters per year
Flux of Sediments	1.4×10^{16} grams per year
Duration of Erosion	1.7×10^{8} years
2. Length of Time to Salt the Sea	
Total Amount of Sodium in Seawater and Salt Deposits:	
Seawater	145×10^{20} grams
Salt Deposits	95×10^{20} grams
Total	240×10^{20} grams
Rate of Supply by Streams	207×10^{12} grams per year
Time to Deliver All the Sodium to the Sea	1.2×10^{8} years

of sodium by streams would raise the salt content of the ocean to the present salinity in about 100 million years (Table 2–1). We now know that the salts of the sea are recycled by reactions as new oceanic crust is formed through the agency of plate tectonics. These rocks are subject to alteration at the convergence of plates through mountain building and volcanism. By these processes the salt content of the oceans can remain fairly constant over time.

Despite the fact that these flawed techniques provided an age of Earth far greater than the short age inferred from historical record, none of these large estimates satisfied the paleontologists and the biologists, and they felt that even more time was required by the slow process of natural selection to achieve the diversification of life observed at the present time. It was not until the introduction of the first application of a radioactive method of dating in 1905 that the prospect for resolving the age problem was established.

THE RADIOACTIVITY CLOCK

Perhaps one of the most exciting applications of the principles of chemistry and physics to the study of Earth and the solar system has been the use of radioactivity to determine geologic time. It is the systematic nature of the radioactive "decay" law that gives it the qualities of a clock.

Any assemblage of neutrons and protons in a nucleus of an atom is called a *nuclide*. Nuclides having the same number of protons but different numbers of neutrons are called *isotopes* of the same element. (Each element is distinguished by the number of protons in the nucleus. For example, carbon (C) has 6 protons in the nucleus. The isotopes of C having 6, 7, or 8 neutrons in the nucleus are designated ^{12}C, ^{13}C, ^{14}C, respectively). Some nuclides are unstable or radioactive and their nuclei reach more stable internal organization by the emission of energetic particles that are the result of transformations within the nucleus itself. Such transformations may be the conversion of a neutron to a proton, the other way around, or the ejection of a cluster of 2 neutrons and 2 protons as common modes of transformation. Although we can identify which nuclides are radioactive, we cannot predict exactly when any one nucleus that is capable of radioactive decay will actually undergo its transformation. Instead we must treat the behavior of a large assemblage of nuclei in a statistical manner (see Appendix 2–1). When we do this we derive the fundamental law of radioactive decay: *The number of radioactive nuclei that decay in a unit time interval is directly proportional to the number of nuclei present at that time.* This law has been verified without exception for every radioactive nuclide studied, and is expressed in mathematical shorthand as

$$\frac{\Delta N}{\Delta t} = -\lambda N$$

where $\Delta N/\Delta t$ is the rate of change with time (Δ is the Greek capital "delta" and means "difference in"), the number N of radioactive nuclei present at that instant, and λ is the *decay constant*, the proportionality constant relating the rate of change to the number of nuclei present. In statistical terms, we may regard λ as being the probability that any radioactive nucleus will decay in the next unit of time. The constant λ is unique for each radioactive nuclide. The negative sign indicates that the size of N is diminishing with time because of the decay. This equation, when written in the proper mathematical form instead of the simple form expressed, can be used to follow the value of N as t increases. The resulting equation is

$$N = N_0 e^{-\lambda t}$$

This type of mathematical expression describes an *exponential decrease* and the base of the exponential scale is the so-called "natural base" e (see Appendix 2–1). The value of e is 2.718. This equation indicates that if we start with a number of radioactive particles N_0 at some time that we designate as time zero, after a length of time t has elapsed the number of particles still remaining is N.

If we take the natural logarithm (base *e*) of the integrated form of the radioactive decay equation we get

$$\ln N = \ln N_0 - \lambda t$$

where "ln" represents the logarithm to the base *e*. (Most hand-held calculators have the ln function for easy solution of problems.) Hence a plot of the logarithm against time will give a straight line (Fig. 2–4). The slope of the line is $-\lambda$.

Sometimes another index of the decay constant is used, the *half-life,* which is the length of time required to diminish the original number of

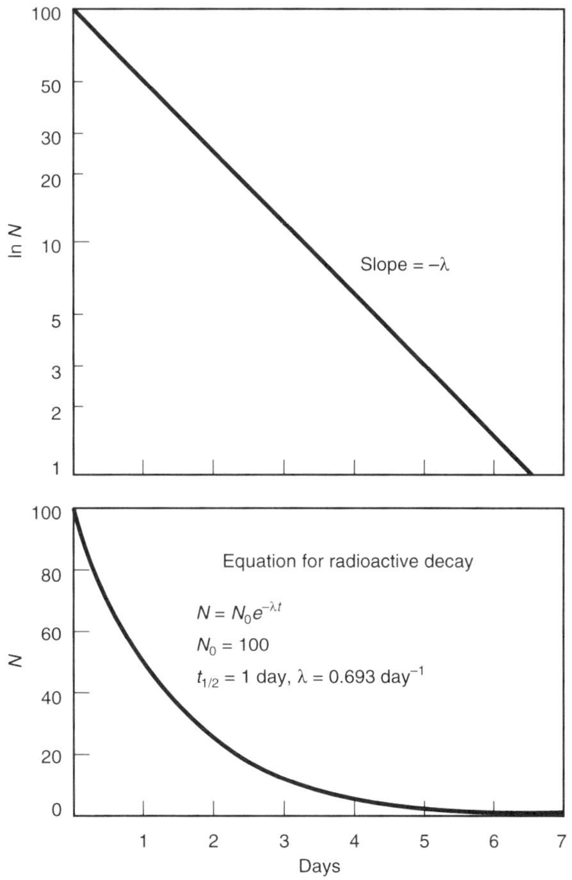

FIGURE 2–4 The radioactive decay curve. Starting with 100 atoms of a radioactive nuclide the number decreases to 50 in 1 day. That is, its half-life is 1 day and $\lambda = 0.693\ \text{day}^{-1}$.

radioactive nuclei by half. By using the above equation it can be shown that the decay constant is related to the half-life ($t_{1/2}$) by the equality $t_{1/2} = 0.693/\lambda$ (where the value 0.693 is the natural logarithm of 2).

RADIOCARBON DATING

We can make a direct application of Figure 2–4 using a naturally produced radioactive isotope of carbon, ^{14}C (carbon-14). The common stable isotope of carbon is ^{12}C; a less common stable isotope of carbon is ^{13}C, about which we will have more to say in later chapters. Radiocarbon (^{14}C) has a half-life of 5730 years and is produced continuously in the atmosphere by cosmic rays. Cosmic rays are high-energy projectiles, composed mainly of hydrogen ions (or protons) of galactic origin. The cosmic rays produce neutrons by reactions with the common gases composing the atmosphere. As the neutrons so produced collide with atmospheric molecules they lose energy so that after they are slowed down to a certain level of energy, they efficiently enter into and react with the nuclei of ^{14}N (nitrogen-14), the most common isotope in the atmosphere. This reaction occurs at about 55,000 ft (17,000 m) elevation in the lower stratosphere.

When this absorption occurs a proton is emitted and ^{14}N is transformed to ^{14}C, radiocarbon. The ^{14}C that is produced quickly reacts with oxygen in the atmosphere to produce $^{14}CO_2$ which behaves like ordinary CO_2 in the processes of photosynthesis and gas exchange with the ocean. The mixing of the $^{14}CO_2$ in the atmosphere is very fast. If there are no changes in the rate of cosmic ray production of radiocarbon and no changes in the supply of ordinary $^{12}CO_2$ to the atmosphere over time, the value of ^{14}C relative to ^{12}C in the atmosphere would remain constant over time. It was this premise that allowed for the possibility of radiocarbon dating.

All systems interacting with the atmospheric CO_2 pool, such as plants and sea shells, would have an initial value of $^{14}C/^{12}C$ determined by the atmosphere. Actually, sea shells deposit $CaCO_3$ from seawater carbonate; because of the slowness of ocean circulation and the decay of ^{14}C when seawater at depth is isolated from the atmosphere prior to upwelling to the surface again, seawater carbonate used by the organism depositing the shell is lower than if the surface seawater were totally in equilibrium with the atmosphere.

A piece of wood, cloth, or leather found in an archaeological site could be dated by using the equation in the previous section or Figure 2–4 constructed for radiocarbon. That is

$$\left(\frac{^{14}C}{^{12}C}\right)_{artifact} = \left(\frac{^{14}C}{^{12}C}\right)_{atmosphere} \times e^{-\lambda_e t}$$

where λ_c is the decay constant for ^{14}C (0.693/5730 y) = ($1.21 \times 10^{-4} y^{-1}$). Reorganizing the equation to obtain an age measured from the present we obtain

$$age(t) = \frac{1}{1.21 \times 10^{-4}} \ln \frac{\left(^{14}C/^{12}C\right)_{atm}}{\left(^{14}C/^{12}C\right)_{artifact}}$$

Actually the $(^{14}C/^{12}C)_{atm}$ has not been constant over time, but the true value can be determined by analyzing precisely dated (by actual counting) tree rings. By relating the calendar year obtained from tree rings to the measured $^{14}C/^{12}C$ in the tree ring, the $(^{14}C/^{12}C)_{atm}$ characteristic of the time can be obtained. With the revised data on the atmospheric $^{14}C/^{12}C$ at the time of formation of the artifact, a very precise date can be obtained.

The method of measurement of radiocarbon in the past was by actual radioactive counting of carbon (thus $^{14}C/^{12}C$, as ^{12}C is the dominant isotope of carbon) extracted from the material to be dated. More and more radiocarbon dates are being measured using nuclear accelerators to measure the atom ratio of ^{14}C to ^{12}C. In that case the accelerator is a way to measure the relative abundances of isotopes of an element and is called a mass spectrometer. With the high sensitivity of this new technique, as little as 10 mg of carbon are required for high-quality dating of the past back to about 40,000 years before the present.

The fundamental restriction on radiocarbon dating is that it is useful only for carbon-bearing materials which derived their carbon ultimately from the atmosphere. In addition to this constraint, the range of dating is limited to the last 40,000 years. Because of radioactive decay, the amount of ^{14}C decreases with time and the amount becomes so small that it cannot be measured with accuracy. Although radiocarbon dating has proven to be the most important dating technique applicable to the study of the recent past (the last 40,000 years), it cannot be used for dating the rocks of Earth and meteorites. We must turn to different isotopes and use a different formulation of the radioactive decay equation.

THE METHODS OF DATING ROCKS AND METEORITES

We start with the premise that we can measure the amount of a radioactive isotope present in a rock today. We cannot determine the amount of radioactive isotope in the rock when it was initially formed but we can measure the amount of the product from its radioactive decay. Over time, as the amount of a radioactive nuclide (called the "parent") decreases, the amount of the stable nuclide formed by the decay (called the "daughter") increases.

Starting with the expression previously given

$$N = N_0 e^{-\lambda t}$$

it is obvious that after a length of time t has elapsed, N atoms of the parent will be left and $N_0 - N$ atoms of the daughter will be formed. Rearranging the equation (that is, dividing through by $e^{-\lambda t}$), we get

$$N_0 = N e^{\lambda t}$$

Subtracting N from both sides

$$N_0 - N = N\,(e^{\lambda t} - 1)$$

and dividing through by N, we obtain

$$\frac{N_0 - N}{N} \quad e^{\lambda t} - 1$$

$N_0 - N$ may be designated d, the number of daughter atoms present today, and N may be designated p, the number of parent atoms remaining today. We can rewrite the above expression explicitly in terms of time:

$$t = \frac{1}{\lambda} \ln\left(\frac{d}{p} + 1\right)$$

The list of radioactive nuclides and their decay products that have been used in dating rocks and meteorites is given in Table 2–2.

THE AGE OF THE SOLAR SYSTEM AND EARTH

We infer the age of the solar system and Earth by studying meteorites. Meteorites were formed early in the history of the solar system and, unlike Earth, most have not been seriously processed by the large-planet forces typical of Earth, such as weathering, melting, and mobilization of the elements. Of the radioactive systems of Table 2–2 the most valuable for dating meteorites is the U-Pb radioactive system.

Meteorites are not all identical in composition. The *chondrites* are agglomerations of primitive material with different degrees of heating and recrystallization at the time of formation. *Achondrites* are meteorites formed by melting on small planetary bodies. This heating, however, took place within a few tens of million years of the origin of the solar system. *Iron meteorites* are segregations of an iron-nickel metal phase associated with melting in the small planetary bodies. All of these meteorite types are relicts of the agglomeration of matter during the formation of the solar system.

TABLE 2–2 Nuclides Commonly Used in Radioactive Geochronometry

Radioactive Isotope	Product	Half-Life (years)
^{238}U	^{206}Pb	4.468×10^9
^{235}U	^{207}Pb	0.704×10^9
^{87}Rb	^{87}Sr	4.881×10^{10}
^{147}Sm	^{143}Nd	1.060×10^{10}
^{40}K (10.5%)	^{40}Ar	1.250×10^9
^{40}K (89.5%)	^{40}Ca	
^{187}Re	^{187}Os	4.560×10^{10}
^{14}C	^{14}N	5730

The dating of the chondrites will give us the earliest age of the solar system-forming process since these meteorite types appear to be less processed by melting than the other two types. Small differences in the chemistry of chondrites also extend to differences in the U/Pb ratio from meteorite to meteorite and, commonly, even among minerals within a chondrite. If chondritic meteorites all formed at the same time, then the changes in the abundances of the daughters of ^{235}U and ^{238}U, ^{207}Pb and ^{206}Pb, respectively, relative to the nonradiogenic background Pb isotopes, will be the consequence of elapsed time and the U/Pb ratios of the individual meteorites. The resulting diagram relating these parameters is known as an *isochron diagram* (Fig. 2–5). Knowing the decay constants of ^{238}U and ^{235}U, a unique age for the group of chondritic meteorites analyzed is precisely determined. This value is 4.55×10^9 years. A similar approach can be taken using the growth of ^{87}Sr from the decay of ^{87}Rb, the growth of ^{143}Nd from the decay of ^{147}Sm, or the growth of ^{187}Os from the decay of ^{187}Re, but the most precise value for the age of the solar system (assuming chondrites are the most primitive members) is obtained from the U-Pb system.

Since achondrites and iron-nickel meteorites are believed to have formed from presumably chondrite-like raw materials by melting and differentiation in small planets within tens of millions of years after chondrites, we can assume that Earth also was formed within the same time scale. The age of the moon, Earth's planetary companion, has been determined and conforms to the old ages of the meteorites.

THE DATING OF CRUSTAL EVENTS

The history of Earth is one of formation of mountains, their erosion, the accumulation of the debris from these processes, and the transformation by

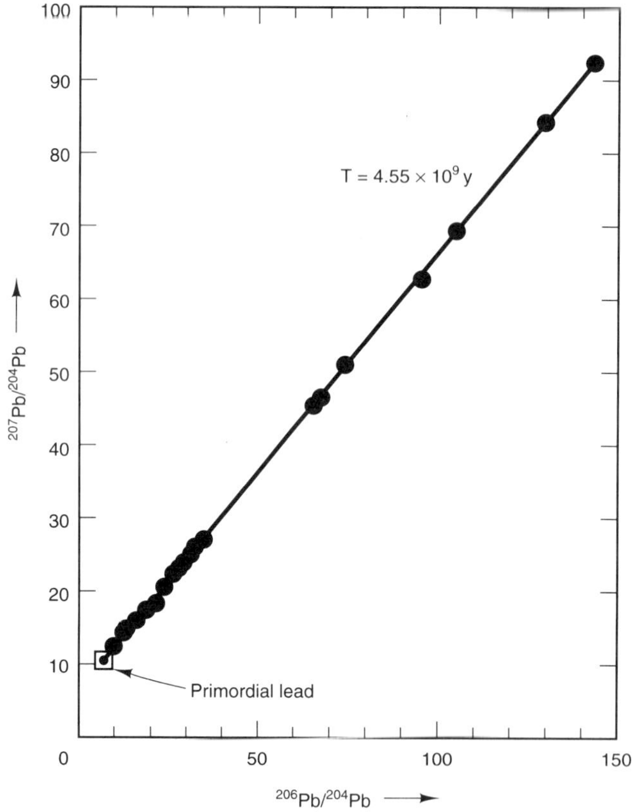

FIGURE 2–5 Lead isotope isochron for the age of meteorites. "Primordial lead" isotopic composition is determined from lead separated from iron sulfide segregates (troilite) in iron meteorites. Troilite has no uranium. The chondritic meteorites each have different ratios of uranium to primoridal lead. After 4.5 billion years the increase in the radiogenic lead isotopes (^{207}Pb and ^{206}Pb) adds to the primary lead composition to yield different values of $^{207}Pb/^{204}Pb$ and $^{206}Pb/^{204}Pb$ for each meteorite. The plot of the two ratios for each meteorite yields a line through the "primary lead" point and the slope provides the age of the assemblage of meteorites as 4.5 billion years. (Data from a number of sources.)

heat and pressure of this processed material; life has developed in response to the changing physical environment. The only record of these events is found in the rocks that are preserved through all these ongoing changes. Where fossils are present, the relative sequence of sedimentary rock layers can be determined in one location and by steps correlated with strata (layers of sedimentary rocks) in other locations. The object of dating rocks by techniques based on radioactivity is to provide a numerical age, or "absolute" chronology, of events like mountain building, and to determine the ages of fossil-bearing strata for determining rates of sediment accumulation and evolution.

Granitic and metamorphic rocks are known by geologists to be associated with the building of mountains resulting from plate tectonic activity. The heat and pressure of the event as well as the mobility of included water in the original rocks result in a reconstruction of the mass of rock to new forms consistent with these forces. Consequently, the implication is that by knowing the ages of these rocks we can thereby date ancient epochs of plate collisions and mountain building. Although old granitic and metamorphic terrains are covered in many places by younger sedimentary rock strata, a large number of dates have been obtained on these "basement" granitic and metamorphic rocks. From these dates it appears that each continent has a mass of very old rocks—about 4 billion years old. In North America the age distribution of granitic and metamorphic rocks can be explained to be the product of plate collisions and episodes of accretion and breaking up—all resulting from the processes of plate tectonics discussed in Chapter 1. The other continents show similar patterns of ages and may be inferred to show the accretionary and breaking-up processes due to plate tectonics.

In the study of Earth's sedimentary rocks, the most important single concept has been that a time sequence can be based on the succession of fossil remains in rocks. Systems of rocks were described and defined from different parts of the world. Often a "system" was defined as the sequence of sedimentary rocks in a large geographic area. A rock system was distinguished by its difference from the surrounding geological or geographic setting. Rocks of the same age from around the world, as interpreted from the fact that they contained similar fossils, could be positioned relative to other systems of rocks. The sequencing of the sedimentary rock systems relative to each other implied that the system of rocks that was beneath another system of rocks was older. From this relationship, a geologic "time scale," or more properly a sequence scale (Table 2–3), was constructed based on the names that were given to each system by the geologists studying them.

The rock systems were described independently by various geologists, and provincial names were used to define them. The *Cambrian* system of rocks was described in Wales (the Roman name for Wales was *Cambria*); the *Ordovician* and *Silurian* systems of rocks were also described in Wales and were named after two ancient tribes that inhabited that region, the *Ordovices* and the *Silures*. The *Devonian* system was first described in the region of Devon in England; the *Mississippian*, along the bluffs of the Mississippi River; the *Pennsylvanian*, from the coal-bearing layers of rocks of Pennsylvania; and the

TABLE 2–3 The Geologic Time Scale

Eon	Era	Period	Epoch	Millions of Years Ago
Phanerozoic	Cenozoic	(Quaternary)	Holocene	0.011
			Pleistocene	1.6
		(Tertiary)	Pliocene	5.1
			Miocene	24
			Oligocene	38
			Eocene	55
			Paleocene	65
	Mesozoic	Cretaceous		144
		Jurassic		200
		Triassic		250
	Paleozoic	Permian		285
		Carboniferous Pennsylvanian		320
		Mississippian		360
		Devonian		410
		Silurian		440
		Ordovician		505
		Cambrian		550
Proterozoic				2500
Archean		Oldest Rock		4000
		Age of the Solar System		4550

Permian, from the region of Perm in Russia. The terms *Triassic*, *Jurassic*, and *Cretaceous* are of continental European origin. *Triassic* means "threefold;" *Jurassic* is named after the Jura Mountains northwest of the Alps, where that system of rocks was first described; and *Cretaceous* means "chalk," referring to calcium carbonate deposits throughout western Europe and England that had types of fossils that were the same, as well as similar physical appearances. (In the United States the Cretaceous is dominated by muddy shales rather than chalky limestones.)

Overlying these rocks were sedimentary rocks with fossils resembling both invertebrate and vertebrate faunas (as well as plants) of the contemporary world. The system of rocks was divided into the younger, generally softer rocks called the *Quaternary,* and the older, less soft rocks called the *Tertiary.* This was based on an outmoded earlier description of rocks where "Primary" rocks of granitic or metamorphic aspect were considered the most primitive. Overlying those rocks in many places were indurated sedimentary rocks called the "Secondary" deposits. The more friable rocks overlying the "Secondary" rocks were the younger "Tertiary" (and "Quaternary") rocks. As the construction of relative positions of rock systems in a sequence developed, the terms "Primary" and "Secondary" were abandoned but the terms "Tertiary" and "Quaternary" stuck.

Each system of rocks is related to a definite time relative to another system of rocks. Therefore each "system" was called a "period" as well. Since the rocks of the Cambrian through the Permian contained fossil remains of invertebrates, such as mollusks and trilobites, as well as primitive vertebrates such as fishes and amphibians, the time represented was called the *Paleozoic ("old life") era* and this time period is sometimes called the "age of fishes." The Triassic, Jurassic, and Cretaceous are called the *Mesozoic ("middle life") era* that is dominated by the rise and spread of reptiles such as the dinosaurs. Because of the presence of almost contemporary looking fossils in the Tertiary and Quaternary strata the two together are called the *Cenozoic ("recent life") era.* Suitably, it is also called the "age of mammals."

The geologic time chart in and of itself tells us nothing about absolute time but rather is a statement of relative sequence. The precise dating of the time chart is accomplished through radioactive geochronometry. This calibration has been developed mainly by the analysis of minerals associated with volcanic deposits intercalated with fossil-bearing strata. In particular, potassium-bearing minerals such as micas and feldspars are used for ^{40}K–^{40}Ar dating and zircons are used for U-Pb dating (since zircons harbor a large amount of U in their crystal structures).

PROBLEM:

A. Radioactive geochronometry etude.

1. Draw the graph for $N_o = 14$ units and $\lambda = 1 \times 10^{-4} y^{-1}$ [y = years].
2. What is the age of a sample having (using your graph):
   (a) $N = 7$
   (b) $N = 1$
3. Draw the curve showing the relationship of d/p to t for:
   (a) $\lambda = 1 \times 10^{-4} y^{-1}$
   (b) $\lambda = 1 \times 10^{-10} y^{-1}$
4. Calculate the age for a radioactive nuclide having $\lambda = 1 \times 10^{-10} y^{-1}$ where:
   (a) $d/p = 0.5$
   (b) $d/p = 1$

B. In April of 1986 the fallout of the Chernobyl reactor accident was monitored at Studsvik, Sweden, by L. Devell and colleagues (*Nature,* 1986, v. 321, p. 192). ^{131}I ($\lambda = 0.086$ day $^{-1}$) and ^{133}I ($\lambda = 0.800$ day^{-1}) were among the radioactive isotopes identified in the fallout. The table below lists the ratio of concentrations of ^{133}I relative to ^{131}I which would have been measured at noon on the given date.

Date	Concentration of ^{133}I Relative to ^{131}I
April 28	0.25
April 29	0.123
April 30	0.0603
May 1	0.0295
May 2	0.0145

1. Plot log ($^{133}I/^{131}I$) vs. day.
2. Given that concentration of ^{133}I relative to $^{131}I = 2.14$ at the time the reactor shut down and that the radioactive cloud resulting from the explosion gradually began impacting Sweden starting on April 28, use your plot to determine the date the reactor shut down.

APPENDIX 2–1: THE LAW OF RADIOACTIVE DECAY

Probability of decay, P, over interval Δt

$$P = \lambda \Delta t$$

Therefore, the probability of survival is

$$1 - P = 1 - \lambda \Delta t$$

where λ is the decay constant. The probability of survival after n intervals of Δt ("this and that" law) is

$$(1 - P)^n = (1 - \lambda \Delta t)^n$$

but

$$t = n\Delta t$$

therefore

$$(1-P)^n = (1- \lambda t\,/n)^n$$

THE NATURAL BASE *e*

Let

$$e^x = \lim_{n\to\infty} (1 + x\,/n\,)^n$$

then for $x = 1$,

$$e = \lim_{n\to\infty} (1 + 1/n)^n$$

and therefore

$$e = 2.718$$

Now let

$$x = -\lambda t$$

then

$$e^{-\lambda t} = \lim_{n\to\infty} (1 - \lambda t/n)^n$$

and in radioactive decay, after time t has elapsed, when N_o atoms decrease to N atoms, the probability of survival of a collection of radioactive atoms after length of time, t, must be:

$$N/N_o = \lim_{n\to\infty} (1 - \lambda t/n)^n = e^{-\lambda t}$$

Therefore

$$N/N_o = e^{-\lambda t}$$

3

THE EVOLUTION OF THE ATMOSPHERE

We have seen in Chapter 1 that the atmospheres of the planets are not all the same. Each planet has an atmosphere determined by the peculiar history of the planet. Such factors as the size of the planet and closeness to the sun act to determine the range of planetary atmospheres we observe today. A unique factor for Earth is the existence of life. No other planet has had this peculiar type of influence on its atmosphere. The evolution of Earth's atmosphere can only be understood by including this dominating fact.

THE PRESENT-DAY COMPOSITION OF THE ATMOSPHERE

The composition of air is the direct consequence of the supply of gaseous elements from Earth's interior and the presence of life. Nitrogen (78% by volume) and oxygen (21% by volume) are the two major gases in the atmosphere and are the result of the actions of organisms. Photosynthesis by plants makes oxygen, which in turn is used in respiration by macroorganisms and microorganisms. Nitrogenous compounds from living organisms are returned as nitrogen to the atmosphere as the result of metabolism (denitrification). Lightning converts atmospheric nitrogen into molecules usable by lifeforms. The third most abundant gas in the atmosphere is argon (1% by volume), a chemically unreactive gas. Argon is dominated by the isotope argon-40 (^{40}Ar) that is produced by the radioactive decay of an isotope of potassium (^{40}K) in rocks (as shown in Chapter 2). The internal heat of Earth releases the accumulating argon-40 in the crust and mantle. The presence of argon in the atmosphere implies that other gases are also supplied to Earth's surface. The composition of our present-day atmosphere is given in Table 3–1. All the other gases in the atmosphere are present in volumetrically small amounts compared to nitrogen, oxygen, and argon (mainly ^{40}Ar). Water and carbon dioxide are variable, minor components of the atmosphere and yet their significance as gases transcends their relatively small concentrations. The two most important roles of these gases are controlling the temperature of Earth's surface and originating and maintaining life.

Water vapor in the atmosphere is primarily the result of evaporation from the ocean surface; the amount in an air column above the sea surface is related to the temperature at the air-sea interface. As the temperature of the surface ocean water increases, the water vapor concentration of air in a column immediately above the water increases as the air temperature seeks to respond to the ocean temperature. Precipitation occurs when air, once in contact with the oceans, is cooled by convection, causing the water vapor concentration to equal the saturation value at a given temperature.

The carbon dioxide concentration in the atmosphere is the direct result of photosynthesis and respiration (see Appendix 3–1). The concentration of carbon dioxide in the atmosphere changes seasonally in the northern hemisphere where most of the land of our planet is presently located. The growth of land plants in late spring and summer extracts carbon dioxide from the air, and storage of leaf litter during the fall and winter maintains the carbon dioxide of the atmosphere at a low level. The increased rate of oxidation of this stored carbon occurs during the early spring as bacterial decomposition increases because of the increase in temperature. This causes an increase in the carbon dioxide concentration of the atmosphere (Fig. 3–1). Imposed on this seasonal cycle we note, in Figure 3–1, a longer term increase in the car-

TABLE 3–1 Composition of Clean, Dry Air Near Sea Level

Component	Content (% by volume)	Molecular Weight
Nitrogen (N_2)	78.084	28.0134
Oxygen (O_2)	20.9476	31.9988
Argon	0.934	39.948
Carbon dioxide (CO_2)	0.0314	44.00995
Neon	0.001818	20.183
Helium	0.000524	4.0026
Krypton	0.000114	83.80
Xenon	0.0000087	131.30
Hydrogen (H_2)	0.00005	2.01594

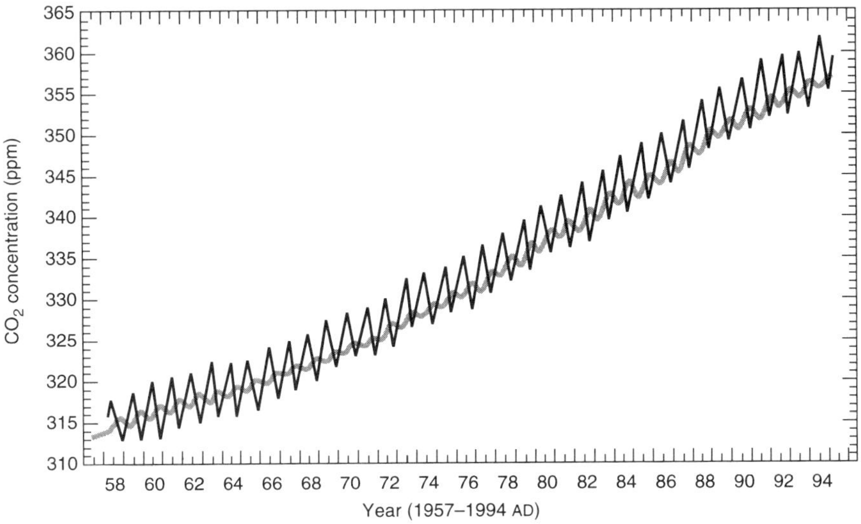

FIGURE 3–1 The variation of the concentration of carbon dioxide in air at Mauna Loa, Hawaii, showing the seasonal pattern of the northern hemisphere resulting from depletion by photosynthesis during spring and summer and oxidation of organic matter during late winter and early spring. There has been an increase in the carbon dioxide concentration in the air over the measurement period. (Data collected by C. D. Keeling and National Oceanic and Atmospheric Administration, Environmental Research Laboratories.)

bon dioxide concentration in the air, which is attributable to the increased burning of fossil fuels starting in earnest about 130 years ago.

The importance of water and carbon dioxide to the sustenance of life is obviously of paramount importance since organic carbon compounds making up living material are composed of carbon, hydrogen, and oxygen to a large extent. Water and carbon dioxide as gases also have the special property of being able to warm Earth's surface through the absorption of radiation. It is this process, commonly called the "greenhouse effect," that we turn to next.

THE STRUCTURE OF THE ATMOSPHERE

As one climbs up into the atmosphere two features are evident: The atmospheric pressure decreases with elevation and the temperature also decreases. The decrease in pressure is due to the fact that the density of molecules (number of molecules per unit volume) is highest close to Earth's surface and decreases outward to space due to the decreasing gravitational pull on the molecules. The reason for decreasing temperature with increasing altitude is that gas cools as it expands.

Although the density of the atmosphere decreases continuously away from Earth's surface, the temperature actually begins increasing again at a certain altitude. The altitude at which this temperature inversion occurs is called the *tropopause.* The region below the tropopause is called the *troposphere* and the region above the tropopause is called the *stratosphere* (Fig. 3–2).

The troposphere is the region in which convection, cloud formation, and precipitation occur. It is heated by the absorption of infrared rays emitted by Earth's surface, the details of which are described in the next section.

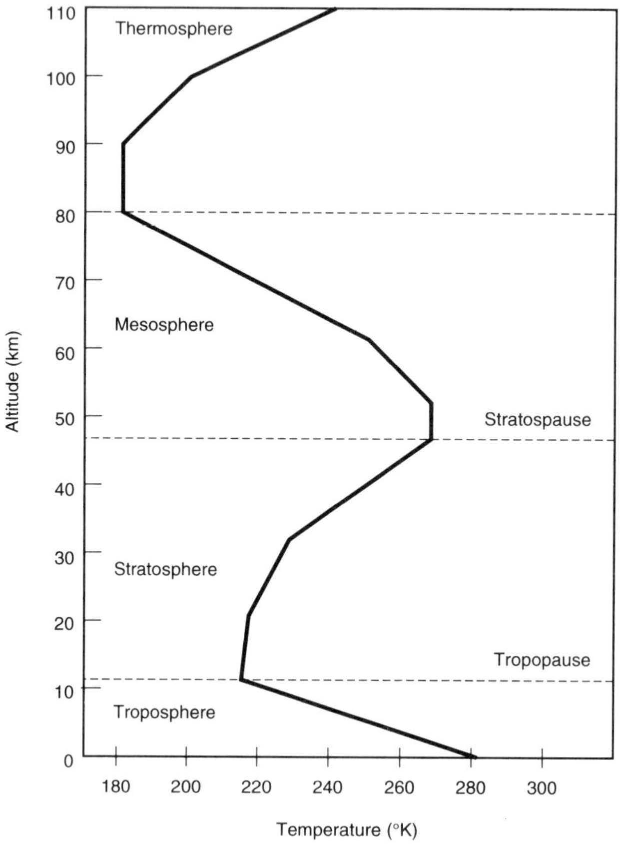

FIGURE 3–2 The temperature structure of Earth's atmosphere. The boundary between the stratosphere and the mesosphere is set at the stratopause, where the formation and destruction of ozone heats the stratospheric air. The thermosphere has so few molecules that warming occurs by the high relative intensity of photons per molecule.

The stratosphere is heated by reactions of gas molecules with the sun's ultraviolet rays.

At the lower part of the troposphere the interaction of the atmosphere with Earth's surface makes it a region of distinctive properties so far as water exchange and turbulence are concerned. This layer is called the *boundary layer*. It is often demarcated by low-lying clouds. The atmosphere in the region bounded by 30° latitude and the equator over the ocean is marked by a sharp boundary at about 3 km called the trade-wind inversion; below this boundary the winds come from the east and above it the winds come from the west.

The height of the tropopause varies with location and season but it is roughly 11 km above the ground surface. The thickness of the boundary layer varies even more frequently than the tropopause. In many places on land it is virtually zero thickness at night and about 0.5 to 1 km thick during the day.

Discussions of global warming refer to the troposphere as the region where weather and climate are made and where the air is in direct contact with the surface.

RADIATIVE BALANCE AND ATMOSPHERIC HEATING—THE "GREENHOUSE EFFECT"

The sun emits light at its surface that is primarily in the visible range of the spectrum: Wavelengths correspond to the rainbow colors of red, orange, yellow, green, blue, indigo, and violet. There is also a significant component of ultraviolet (shorter wavelength than violet) light and infrared (longer wavelength than red) light (Fig. 3–3). One can imagine light to be the result of the transport of particles called photons. The greater the flux of photons, the greater the intensity of light. The intensities of light rays along the continuum of wavelengths we call the spectrum are related to the wavelength. The maximum intensity is in the region of yellow-green light. The intensity drops off toward both the ultraviolet and infrared ends of the spectrum. Why does this pattern exist? Intensity of light is not to be confused with the energy characteristic of each wavelength of light. As the wavelength decreases (toward the ultraviolet, for example) the energy increases. This distribution can be understood in terms of the concept of the "black body radiator" (Appendix 3–2). If a black body (ideally a chamber with a pinhole for the light from the inside to emerge for observation) is increased in its temperature, it will progressively change from a body emitting primarily infrared light at the lowest temperatures to domination by visible and ultraviolet light at the high temperatures characteristic of the sun (~6000°C). Thus as temperature increases, the most intense

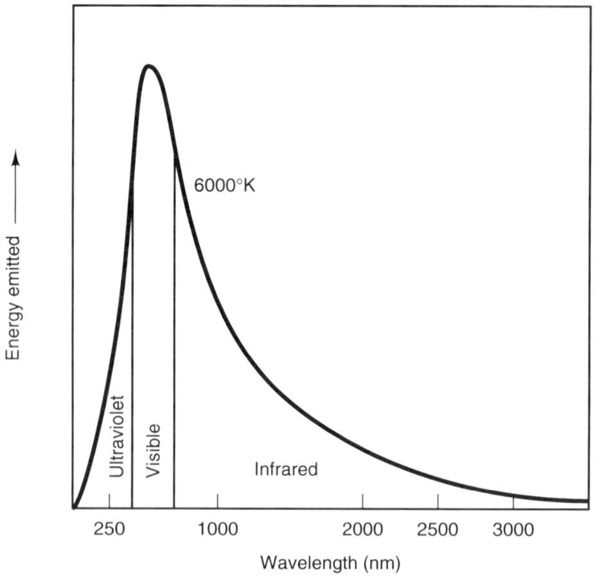

FIGURE 3–3 We break the spectrum of sunlight into ultraviolet, visible, and infrared radiation, the former having a shorter wavelength than the latter. Most of the energy of the radiation is visible and 95% of the total energy lies between 250 and 2500 nano-meters (that is, 10^{-9} meters or nm).

light has a wavelength that becomes shorter and shorter, that is more toward the ultraviolet (Fig. 3–4). Earth is bombarded primarily by visible wavelength light with some ultraviolet (and infrared) light. Most of the visible light passes through the atmosphere without significant attenuation. It is in part reflected back to outer space by clouds, ice fields, and deserts. That which is not reflected is absorbed at Earth's surface. As it is absorbed by the rock and soil at the surface, the ground warms and emits radiation primarily in the infrared, as if it were a black body with an average temperature of 300°K (Fig. 3–5).

Unlike ultraviolet and visible light, infrared light is strongly absorbed by the water and carbon dioxide molecules in the air. As these molecules absorb the infrared energy they transform part of this energy into motion energy and collide with the dominant gases of the atmosphere, nitrogen, oxygen, and argon, and they too speed up. The total increase of energy of motion of all the molecules of gas in the air increases the temperature of the gas even though the energy absorption started with carbon dioxide and water. Thus carbon dioxide and water are referred to as "greenhouse gases" and are almost uniquely responsible for warming the lower atmosphere (the troposphere).

The atmosphere, heated through the absorption of infrared radiation by carbon dioxide and water, also emits infrared radiation characteristic of its

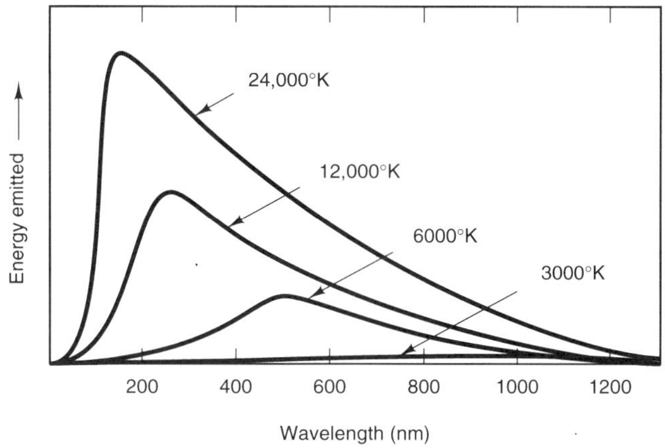

FIGURE 3–4 Energy emitted at different wave lengths for black bodies at several temperatures.

temperature. We can imagine the atmosphere as being made of layers of gas through which the infrared radiation emitted by Earth's surface passes on its return to space. Half the radiation (or photon) flux in each of these layers is upward and half downward. The layer closest to the ground tends to be the warmest as it receives not only the radiation from the ground but also from

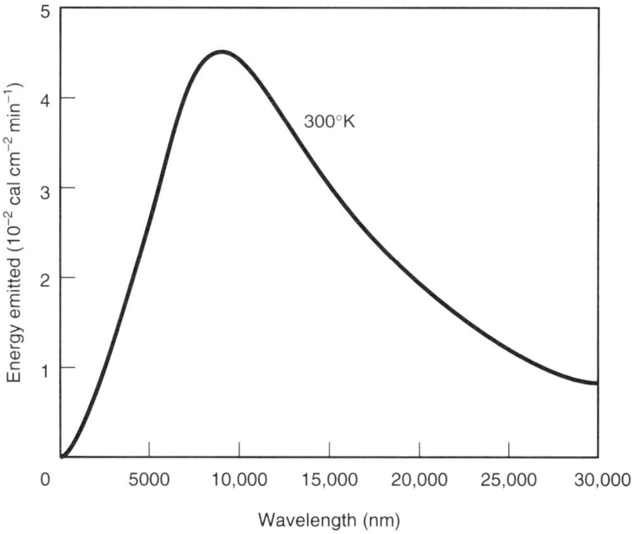

FIGURE 3–5 The emission of light from Earth's surface depends on the temperature. A black body temperature of 300°K radiates mainly between 2500 and 25,000 nm (in the infrared).

the heated atmosphere layers above, whereas the higher layers lose radiation progressively to space.

This radiative balance would result in a thermal structure of the troposphere in which the warmest air is found at the ground surface with the troposphere getting progressively cooler with altitude (Fig. 3–6). Imposed on the radiative balance, however, is convective motion of the blanket of air due to the enhanced warming of the bottom of the troposphere. As one ascends higher and higher in the atmosphere, the air becomes more and more rarified due to diminished gravitational attraction. As air is transported upward by convection from the ground surface, it is cooled by expansion; when it descends to a zone of higher pressure closer to the ground surface, it is warmed. The result is the modification of the thermal structure demanded by radiative equilibrium, but still the warmest air is maintained at sea level, the lowest layer in an idealized planetary surface (Fig. 3–6).

THE ORIGIN OF THE ATMOSPHERE

We start with the premise that whatever gases were present on or in Earth as it was formed, the atmospheric composition was modified by the great collision of a Mars-sized body with primitive Earth, resulting in the moon-Earth system

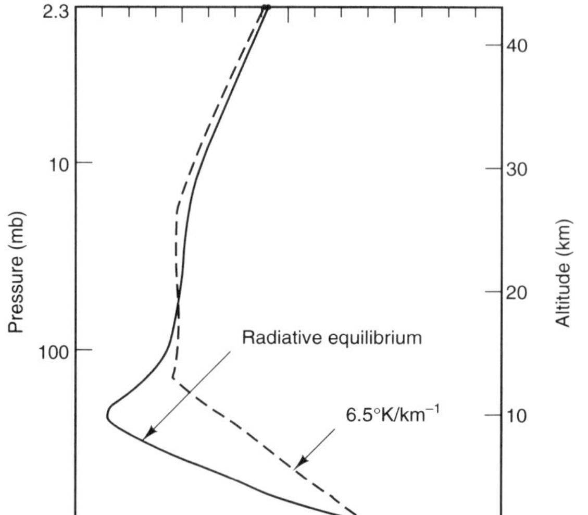

FIGURE 3–6 The variation of temperature with altitude in a radiative equilibrium model assuming: (1) pure radiative equilibrium only, and (2) convection and precipitation occurring, resulting in a lapse rate (or decrease in temperature with increasing altitude) of 6.5°K km^{-1}. (After S. Manabe and R. F. Strickler, 1964, *J. Atmos. Sci.* v. 21, p. 361. American Meterological Society.)

as discussed in Chapter 1. Any gases in the atmosphere or released from Earth by the energy of the collision would be subject to loss from Earth's gravity field. We know that Earth's interior has been releasing gas to the surface ever since that collision event not only from the presence of argon-40 in the atmosphere, as discussed, but also the discovery of the release of a rare isotope of helium, another unreactive gas (helium-3 or ^3He), from submarine vents (Fig. 3–7). It is possible, through the analysis of the so-called rare gases, to

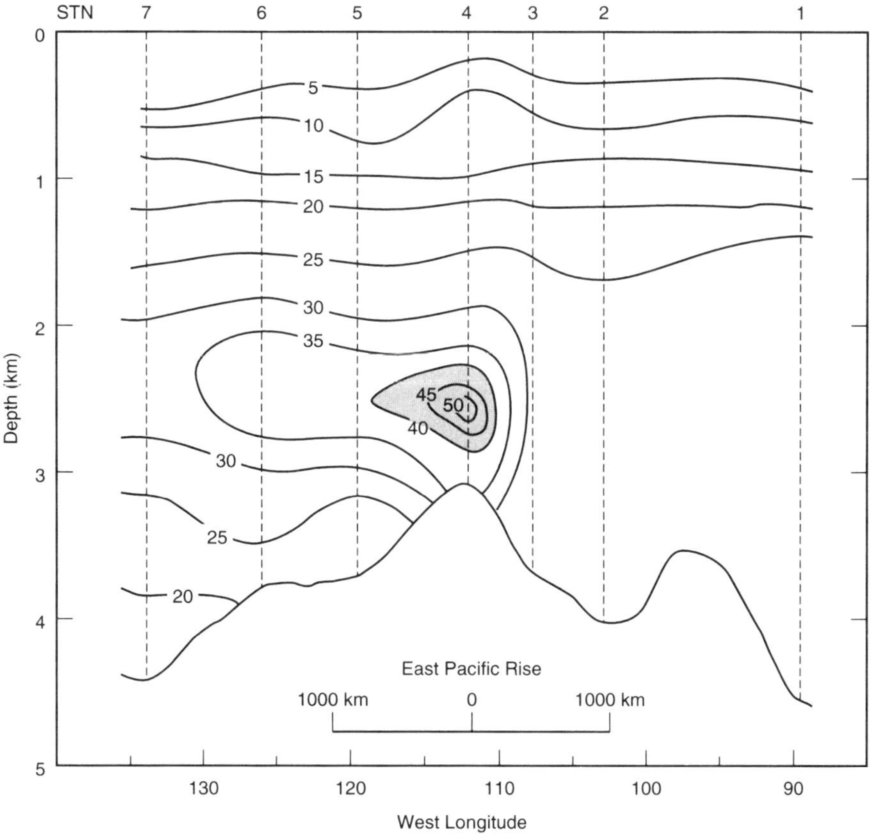

FIGURE 3–7 A section across the East Pacific Rise in the South Pacific showing ^3He in excess over that expected from the solution of atmospheric ^3He when scaled to the more common ^4He. The difference between dissolved He isotopic ratio and atmospheric He is represented by δ^3He in percent difference. ^3He is assumed to be primordial and indicates degassing of the mantle at the divergent plate boundaries featured as oceanic ridge systems. STN = station number of the sampling. (Reprinted with permission from J. E. Lupton and H. Craig, 1981, *Science,* v. 214, p. 1564. Copyright American Association for the Advancement of Science.)

decipher the processes of atmosphere formation. These unreactive gases found in the atmosphere and in rocks derived from the mantle include helium, neon, argon, krypton, and xenon.

The evidence from which we construct a history of the atmosphere and oceans comes from a number of sources. First, we have an idea of the total amount of water on Earth's surface not only in the main reservoir of the oceans but also in ice caps and in ground and surface waters tied up in crustal rocks (Table 3–2). We note that the ratio of a rare heavy isotope of hydrogen deuterium (written as D or ^{2}H), relative to the dominant isotope of hydrogen (^{1}H or simply H), on Earth is much greater than in the sun. Next, we sum up all the carbon in the atmosphere, oceans, and the crust (in the form of limestone, oil, coal, natural gas, and sedimentary rocks rich in organic matter.) The carbon to hydrogen ratio of Earth's surface is found to be considerably higher than that found in the sun. A third observation is the relative abundances of the rare gases in the atmosphere compared to the solar composition (Fig. 3–8). We note also that for the rare gases, krypton and xenon, for which there are many isotopes, the heavier isotopes are more abundant than the light isotopes. The relationship of the masses of the gases to their abundances indicates that some process of preferential loss of the less massive rare gases or, for individual rare gases, their isotopes has occurred during the formation of the atmosphere. We note without further exposition here that only helium is lost from our atmosphere at the present time.

On the basis of the hydrogen (mainly as water), carbon (mainly as limestone and organic matter associated with sedimentary rocks), and rare gas patterns, the following scenario of the early formation of the atmosphere can be constructed. As Earth accreted, it trapped gases in roughly the proportion found in the sun. The exact process of incorporation is not known but may resemble the implanting of solar flare gases in soils of the moon or in collectors deployed on the moon by our astronauts. During the process of Earth's accumulation some gases may have been released to the atmosphere where

TABLE 3–2 Mass of the Present Hydrosphere

	Total Mass (units of 10^{20} g)	Percentage of Total Hydrosphere
Oceans	13,700	80.0
Pore waters in sediments	3,300	18.8
Ice	200	1.2
Rivers, lakes	0.3	0.002
Atmosphere	0.13	0.0008
Total hydrosphere	17,200	100.0

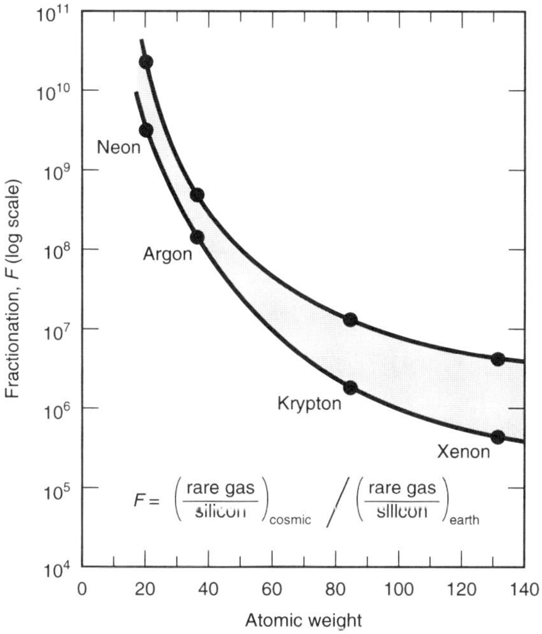

FIGURE 3–8 The fractionation of the rare gases with respect to silicon in Earth relative to the primitive solar nebula. The shaded area represents the uncertainties in the cosmic ratios. (After H. Brown, 1952, in *The Atmospheres of the Earth and Planets,* ed. G. P. Kuiper, University of Chicago Press.)

they remained because of the gravitational pull of the accreting planet. When Earth reached roughly its present size and had undergone significant fractionation into an iron-metal core and a silicate mantle, many scientists believe it was struck by a Mars-sized body. The energy of collision raised the surface temperature temporarily to values as high as 16,000°K! This high temperature caused most of the gas in the primitive atmosphere or in the upper mantle to escape from the planet. The lightest gases and the light isotopes of each gaseous element were preferentially lost, resulting in a smaller, mass-fractionated atmosphere. The deep interior of the planet retained the gases roughly in solar proportions and not significantly mass-fractionated.

Under the early conditions of high temperatures at Earth's surface the dominant gas in the atmosphere was water vapor. As radiative cooling occurred the water condensed into oceans, the size of which probably exceeded that of the present-day oceans. The sun's rays are now responsible for keeping Earth's surface warm. The Sun has had this same role throughout Earth's history. The radiant output of the sun, however, was about 30% lower 4.5 billion years ago than it is today (Fig. 3–9), so that Earth's surface would have been cooler at that time if the atmospheric composition was similar. Some planetary scientists believe that Earth's surface could have had a frozen water-ice veneer. Once ice was formed its reflectivity of the sun's rays would diminish the radiation absorbed by Earth's surface and therefore its temperature. The frozen planetary surface theory would not permit significant warming and melting of the ice even as the sun's heat output increased to the present value. The way out of this apparent dilemma depends on the special greenhouse properties of carbon dioxide.

Because of the low abundance of carbon in the solar material relative to hydrogen, and because carbon dioxide, or more probably methane, would behave like water, neon, or argon, whatever carbon-bearing gases existed would have been lost from the planet at the time of the moon-forming collision. Yet the carbon content of the surface of Earth is considerably higher now than this expectation would allow.

It is for this reason that the addition of cometary-like material rich in organic material after the moon-forming impact is required. These impacts

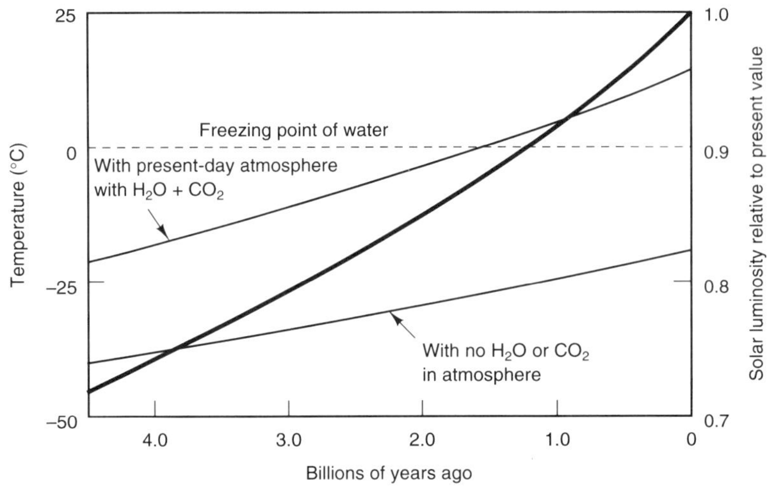

FIGURE 3–9 The changing luminosity of the sun over time and the corresponding temperature of Earth's surface assuming no atmosphere and the present-day atmosphere. Increasing the water vapor would raise the temperature at Earth's surface but the clouds formed at high elevations would increase the albedo of the planet and thereby act to diminish the temperature. If the freezing temperature is not exceeded, Earth's surface would be covered by ice. Melting would occur by the addition of dark cometary material and the supply of carbon converting to carbon dioxide.

influence the composition of the atmosphere and ultimately the temperature of Earth's surface.

One group of meteorites called *carbonaceous chondrites* contains 20% water in minerals and 5% carbon in a variety of compounds ranging from fine diamond-like dust to complex organic compounds. This latter material could provide the building blocks for life on Earth. These meteorites are thought to be related to cometary cores. This type of impacting body would provide a veneer of carbon to Earth, which on oxidation would ultimately become carbon dioxide.

The putative, ice-covered Earth existing prior to the rain of cometary material was then transformed, since methane or carbon dioxide will not freeze out even at the low temperatures postulated to form water-ice. Thus these gases performed their roles as greenhouse agents in the atmosphere even though the vapor pressure of water over ice would have been low. As the temperature at the surface increased the ice would melt. Once this occurred water vapor would increase and this in turn would greatly increase the warming of the planet by absorbing more of the heat generated at Earth's surface by the sun's rays.

An atmosphere with a large amount of carbon dioxide would have an enhanced effect on the temperature of Earth's surface. By considering the planet Venus, we can see what might have happened if all of the carbon on Earth stayed in the atmosphere as carbon dioxide. Venus presently has an atmosphere composed of almost pure carbon dioxide at 100 times the amount of the total atmosphere of Earth. The surface temperature of Venus is a forbidding 400°C! The amount of carbon on the Venutian surface is about the same as the amount that is on Earth. Therefore it follows that if all the carbon on Earth were in the form of carbon dioxide, the temperature of Earth's surface would be similar to Venus and life could not have formed on the planet. How did the control of the level of carbon dioxide on our planet occur so that the story of life could begin?

Pulverized rock from impacts and glacial grinding, in the presence of water, acts to take up the carbon dioxide by reaction with the surfaces of the pulverized grains. The sodium, potassium, magnesium, and calcium, which are common elements in surface rocks, will be released from the highly pulverized rock by reaction with water. The hydrogen ions in the water are exchanged for these cations in the rock and the solution becomes highly alkaline. As such, the alkaline solution aggressively absorbs the carbon dioxide from the air sufficiently to decrease the carbon dioxide content of the atmosphere. This process is active today. If no life processes or renewed supplies of carbon dioxide were involved, the amount of carbon dioxide would be controlled by this reaction to levels dictated by the temperature (see Appendix 3–1). With the decrease in this greenhouse gas, the surface temperature of Earth decreases to one more equitable for life. The temperature need not have been as cool as the present-day surface for life to begin and thrive. Early bacteria-like organisms could have been thermophilic ("heat-loving") based on genetic studies of their evolved progeny. Such thermophilic bacteria are found at hot springs such as those in Yellowstone Park and in oceanic hydrothermal vents. Venus is sufficiently close to the Sun so that the surface temperature always remained high. Water was lost and the carbon dioxide was not efficiently removed in a dry environment.

HOW THE MASS AND COMPOSITION OF THE ATMOSPHERE CHANGED WITH TIME

The masses of the atmosphere and the seas of our planet have changed with time. Nitrogen, carbon, and water were present at the surface of Earth from its earliest days, and they are continuously being released from Earth's interior. Why would these volatiles escape from Earth's interior if they were trapped there since the time of its formation? The answer to this question lies in the fact that Earth must release the heat acquired during the accretion process and release heat from the ongoing radioactive decay of uranium, thorium, and potassium. Plate tectonics requires that crust be transported back into the mantle at convergence plate boundaries. With this transfer there must be some transport of chemically reactive gases like CO_2 and water associated with the altered crustal rocks. Thus a cycling of chemically reactive gases between Earth's surface and its mantle must be occurring continuously.

Vivid examples of this process are seen in Yellowstone Park, where the geysers and hot springs transport heat from depth to the surface. Similar hot water vents are found along the great, world-encircling ridges in the oceans where volcanic emanations and deep oceanic hot springs show the locations of the rising column of hot, deep mantle in the grand convective cycle of Earth's interior. The returned cooled part of the convective cycle is found at certain ocean-continent margins. The deep trenches and strong explosive volcanic activity in the Andes, the states of Washington and Oregon, the Aleutians, Japan, the Philippines, and Indonesia all are indicators of the energy released at the return to Earth's interior of cooled rock laden with reactive gases, such as water and carbon dioxide.

As we have discussed earlier in this chapter, the water content of the atmosphere is controlled mainly by the saturation of air with water at the temperature of the air-sea interface followed by precipitation during nighttime cooling and cooling resulting during ascent of the air. At Earth's surface, most of the carbon and one-third of the nitrogen are found in the crust: carbon in the form of limestone and organic material in sedimentary rocks; nitrogen mainly as organic material in sedimentary rocks. Fluctuations in the concentrations of nitrogen and carbon in the atmosphere reflect the balance of storage in sediments as the result of life processes and release during exposure and weathering as well as the supply from and loss to the interior of Earth.

THE UNIQUENESS OF ATMOSPHERIC OXYGEN

The history of atmospheric oxygen is controlled by the processes of life. In the first 400 million years of our planet's existence, bacteria-like organisms developed using the available organic matter from chemical syntheses on Earth or from cometary infalls. These early single-celled creatures could take advantage of the sun's light energy, the warmth of Earth's surface, and the presence of water and carbon dioxide to thrive and initiate photosynthesis. In the process of photosynthesis, respiration and biologically mediated rock destruction, precipitates of calcium carbonate were formed much as contemporary deposits are formed in the warm waters of the Bahamas or the shallow marginal seas of Australia. These calcium carbonate deposits resulting from the action of life processes are called *stromatolites,* and many contain records of the earliest forms of life. The morphologies are those of primitive unicellular organisms—the *cyanobacteria.*

In the beginning, virtually all oxygen made by photosynthesis was used up by the oxidation of iron- and sulfide-bearing minerals composing the lavas erupting from Earth's interior, as well as the gases such as hydrogen sulfide and methane associated with the transfer of material from the mantle to the crust. Evidence for the efficient uptake of the oxygen is seen in thinly laminated chemical deposits of iron oxides in shallow ocean platform sediments deposited 2 billion years or more ago. These characteristic deposits are called "banded iron formations" and they occur on continents throughout the world. The sulfate concentration of the oceans also grew, providing the necessary ingredient for sulfate-reducing bacteria (the kind that produce hydrogen sulfide—the "rotten egg" smell compound) proliferating in the absence of oxygen. As a result, iron sulfide deposits were formed and preserved in rocks. The secondary oxidation of these sulfide deposits also helped maintain a low oxygen concentration as long as the organic material formed by photosynthesis was always available. With the increasing proliferation of life, the amount of photosynthesis increased, and the rate of making free oxygen eventually exceeded the rate of oxidation of unburied organic matter, either directly or through the steps involving sulfate-reducing bacteria and the rate of oxidation of mantle-derived iron- and sulfide-bearing minerals. At that point a major global change occurred—the maintenance of an oxygen-rich atmosphere as the result of photosynthesis without concomitant removal by oxidation.

After this time sedimentary rocks generally showed the effects of oxidation. The presence of oxidizable iron in the oceans was greatly attenuated and the special types of sediments nourished from this source, the banded iron formations, all but disappeared. No other planet has significant free oxygen in the atmosphere because no other planet has life. The consequences of this transformation were dramatic. The bacteria-like life (prokaryotes) that dominated Earth until the oxygen level increased strongly, evolved to occupy both oxygen-poor and some oxygen-enriched environments, but a new type of life developed as well. Cells with nuclei in which the genetic material is found (eukaryotes) developed with the special property of depending on atmospheric oxygen for the formation of complex compounds, such as sterols. The eukaryotes are now represented by all of the nonbacterial forms of life from fungi to humans. The common characteristic of eukaryotes is that they absolutely need oxygen to survive and they reproduce by sexual means rather than the asexual reproduction mode of the prokaryotes. The record of eukaryotes has been extended back to about 2.1 billion years ago by the discovery in banded iron formations of forms resembling some modern marine algae. A variety of types of evidence found in ancient rocks indicate that the transition from an oxygen-poor atmosphere to an oxygen-rich atmosphere began about 2.5 billion years ago. The increase of oxygen to values resembling the present levels may have taken 1 billion years.

The oxygen level of the atmosphere over the past 1.5 billion years has been modulated by differences in the rate of photosynthesis and storage of carbon and the rate of oxidation, principally of organic matter. Slight changes in either of these rates will alter the oxygen content of the atmosphere. Small changes in the oxygen content of the atmosphere over the past few years have been observed, perhaps due to the increased burning of fossil fuels, and larger changes have been inferred to have occurred about 300 million years ago associated with the formation of the vast coal deposits. Yet the history of life as seen in the paleontologic record appears to indicate that once the present level of oxygen was attained in the atmosphere it was maintained with only small fluctuations. The maximum range suggested is between 15% and 30% O_2, compared to the present-day value of 21%.

We know that life proceeded from the simple isolated eukaryote cells, typical of algae, to more complex aggregates of cells in colonies such as present-day corals. Finally single organisms with differentiated cells performing specific tasks were developed. The remains of these multicellular organisms, or metazoa (literally, "animals"), were definitely observed as fossil remains in rocks dating about 550 million years ago. There is some sense that metazoa must have existed before this time. The fossils of late Pre-Cambrian age, thought by some to be the first evidence for metazoa, are found in sedimentary rocks throughout the world but were first identified in the Ediacara Formation of Australia and are therefore commonly called the Ediacaran fauna. These organisms lived several tens of million years before the Cambrian age.

THE INTEGRATED HISTORY OF THE ATMOSPHERE

In summary, a guess at the composition of the atmospheric composition over time is presented in Figure 3–10. The initial high carbon dioxide content of the atmosphere was first diminished by reaction with powdered rock in an aqueous medium. As the carbon dioxide content of the atmosphere

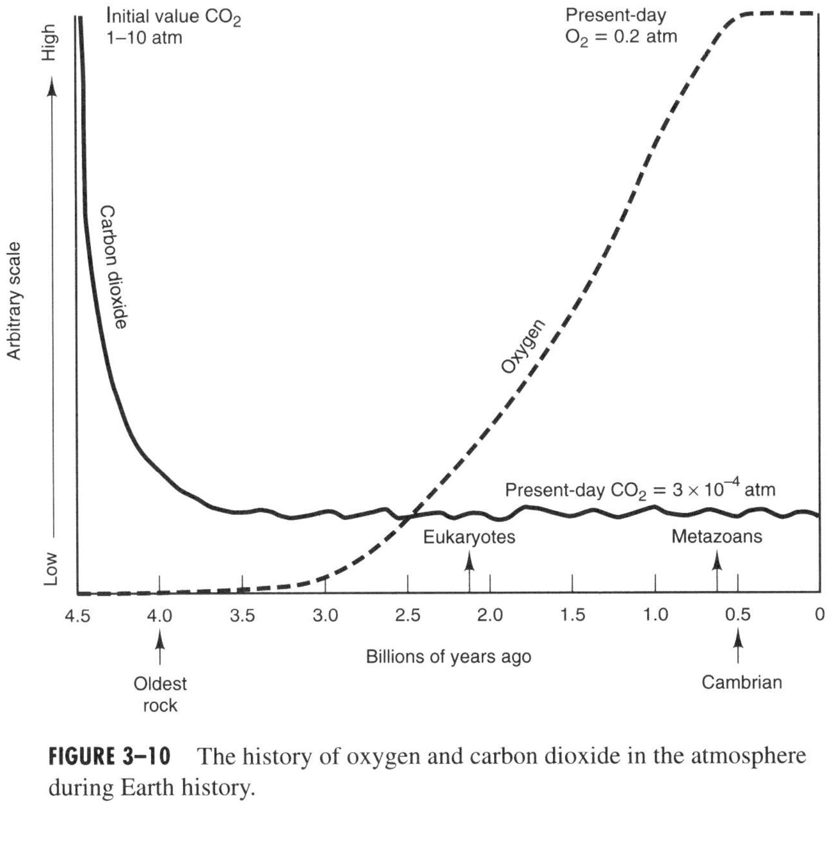

FIGURE 3–10 The history of oxygen and carbon dioxide in the atmosphere during Earth history.

diminished sufficiently to drop the temperature at the surface of Earth, photosynthetic prokaryote life developed and the carbon dioxide content was maintained by respiration and photosynthesis. The amount of free oxygen available is the balance of production by photosynthesis and utilization by oxidation of biologically produced organic matter. The small amount of excess oxygen resulting from the burial of organic matter was at first consumed in the oxidation of reduced iron and sulfur compounds arriving from Earth's interior in conjunction with convective cooling. As photosynthesis and organic compound burial increased, the available oxygen began to increase faster than the rate of consumption by mantle-derived chemical species. The oxygen level then was maintained primarily by photosynthesis and respiration. The carbon dioxide level was also maintained primarily by the same life-controlled process but perturbations due to enhanced direct chemical weathering, changes in solution in seawater, and the control of plate tectonic supply and sequestering of carbon are also evidenced. The nitrogen level in the atmosphere is virtually, exclusively controlled by the denitrification (that is, the reduction of nitrate to molecular nitrogen by organisms) under oxygen-depleted conditions and by the production of nitrogen oxides in the air by lightning caused by the reaction of molecular nitrogen and oxygen. The nitrogen and oxygen concentrations of the atmosphere have remained virtually constant over the past 1.5 billion years, as the result of this balance of processes.

PROBLEM:

A. If the flux of heat from the sun absorbed at the equator is 1 calorie per minute per cm^2, how many days would it take to increase the temperature of a column of water 1 cm^2 by 100 meters deep by 1°C (Celsius or centigrade) if it takes 1 calorie ($= 4.18 \times 10^7$ ergs) to raise the temperature of 1 gram of water 1°C and if no heat were lost from the system? (The density of water is 1 gram per cubic centimeter.)

B. If the initial temperature of surface water were 25°C, what is the radiative flux of heat from the ocean surface? (Remember the Stefan-Boltzmann equation for a black body radiator: $\sigma = 5.672 \times 10^{-5}$ ergs sec^{-1} cm^{-2} $°K^{-4}$).

C. With this correction for radiative heat loss, how long would it take to achieve the temperature increase of question A?

D. If the temperature of surface seawater in the tropics remains essentially constant, what processes would be responsible for this constancy?

APPENDIX 3–1: MODEL REACTIONS INVOLVING CARBON DIOXIDE AND WATER

1. Photosynthesis is the conversion of carbon dioxide and water to oxygen and organic matter by organisms having chlorophyll and that are capable of harnessing the energy from the sun. This reaction is written

$$CO_2 + H_2O \xrightarrow{h\nu} \underset{\text{(sugar, starch, etc.)}}{CH_2O} + O_2$$

   where $h\nu$ = photon energy.

2. The reaction of CO_2 with rock was formally written in the following manner by the Nobel Prize chemist Harold C. Urey, and is therefore called the "Urey Reaction"

$$\underset{\text{(rock representation)}}{CaSiO_3} + CO_2 = CaCO_3 + SiO_2$$

   For example:

   - At 25°C the pressure of CO_2 for this equilibrium is 1.3×10^{-7} atmospheres.
   - At 125°C the pressure of CO_2 for this equilibrium is 8.2×10^{-4} atmospheres.
   - The present-day atmosphere concentration of 3×10^{-4} atmospheres of CO_2, however, is controlled by photosynthesis and respiration rather than the Urey reaction.

3. Precipitation of $CaCO_3$ from seawater occurs as the result of the lowering of dissolved CO_2 by photosynthesis. Seawater has calcium and inorganic carbon as Ca^{++} and H_2CO_3 (CO_2 dissolved in water), carbonate ion ($CO_3^{=}$) and bicarbonate ion (HCO_3^-). At a pH of 7.7 the dominant inorganic form is HCO_3^-. It dissociates according to

$$2HCO_3^- = H_2CO_3 + CO_3^{=}$$

$$H_2CO_3 = H_2O + CO_2$$

   As CO_2 is extracted for photosynthesis, HCO_3^- is converted to $CO_3^{=}$ to maintain equilibrium. As $CO_3^{=}$ concentration increases, the solubility product constant of $CaCO_3$ is exceeded and it precipitates.

4. Oxygen is removed from the atmosphere by the following general reactions:

   - respiration: $O_2 + CH_2O \rightarrow CO_2 + H_2O$
   - "rusting": $2FeO + \frac{1}{2} O_2 \rightarrow Fe_2O_3$
   - oxidation of sulfide: $H_2S + 2O_2 \rightarrow H_2SO_4$

   If organic matter is not oxidized by metabolism, oxygen can accumulate in the atmosphere. This can occur by organic matter burial in sediments.

If FeO and H_2S are supplied from the mantle, oxygen will be removed by "rusting" and sulfide oxidation. If oxygen production by photosynthesis is not used up by the above reactions, oxygen will accumulate in the atmosphere.

APPENDIX 3–2: BLACK BODY TEMPERATURES

Sun's total luminosity:	3.8×10^{33} ergs sec^{-1}
Distance:	Sun–Earth $= 1.49 \times 10^{13}$ cm
Area of sphere at Earth's distance:	2.8×10^{27} cm^2

"Solar Constant":

$$= \frac{\text{total luminosity}}{\text{surface of sphere}}$$

$$= \frac{3.8 \times 10^{33} \text{ ergs sec}^{-1}}{2.8 \times 10^{27} \text{ cm}^2}$$

$$= 1.36 \times 10^{6} \text{ ergs sec}^{-1} \text{ cm}^{-2}$$

The temperature of a black body radiator

energy flux $= \sigma T^4$

σ = Stefan-Boltzmann constant

$= 5.672 \times 10^{-5}$ ergs sec^{-1} cm^{-2} $^{\circ}$K^{-4}

T = degrees on the Kelvin scale

For Earth, energy flux $= 1.36 \times 10^6$ ergs/sec/cm^2

As a disk facing the sun:	temperature = 393.6°K (= 120°C)
As a sphere:	energy flux $= \dfrac{1.36 \times 10^6}{4}$ ergs sec^{-1} cm^{-2}
Since:	area of circle $= \pi r^2$
and	area of sphere $= 4 \pi r^2$

Earth has an albedo of 0.39, therefore the energy flux reaching Earth's surface is modified by a factor of $(1 - 0.39) = 0.61$.

Energy flux to Earth's surface is: $\dfrac{0.61 \times 1.36 \times 10^6}{4}$ ergs sec^{-1} cm^{-2}

As the same energy flux must be returning to space, the black body temperature of Earth = 246°K (= –27°C). Obviously something else must determine the surface temperature. It is the absorption of infrared rays by H_2O and CO_2.

4

TEMPERATURE VARIATION OVER TIME

The temperature at the surface of Earth is determined by three factors: (1) the absolute amount of radiation from the sun; (2) the fraction of the incoming radiation that is reflected, without absorption, from the planetary atmosphere and surface—the planet's albedo; and (3) the composition of the atmosphere as far as the "greenhouse" gases are concerned. All three factors have varied over the history of Earth. Scientists have sought ways to determine the temperature of the past and to predict future temperature variations of the atmosphere. In this chapter we discuss the variations in temperature over time inferred by various techniques.

In order to obtain information about past temperatures on Earth, we need reliable recorders. A written record describing ambient environmental conditions or perhaps a series of consecutive temperature readings (Fig. 4–1) recorded over the years are the most direct ways of knowing about the past. From prehistoric times and back through the eons of geologic time, we must rely on surrogates of temperature preserved in rocks, sediments, and other deposits with a chronology. The more ancient the record, the more likely is it to be blurred by processes of alteration and obliteration that are characteristic of our changing planet, thus making the extraction of a suitable record increasingly more difficult the farther back in time we go. We will restrict our exploration of temperature variations, therefore, to the more recent past of the geologic record.

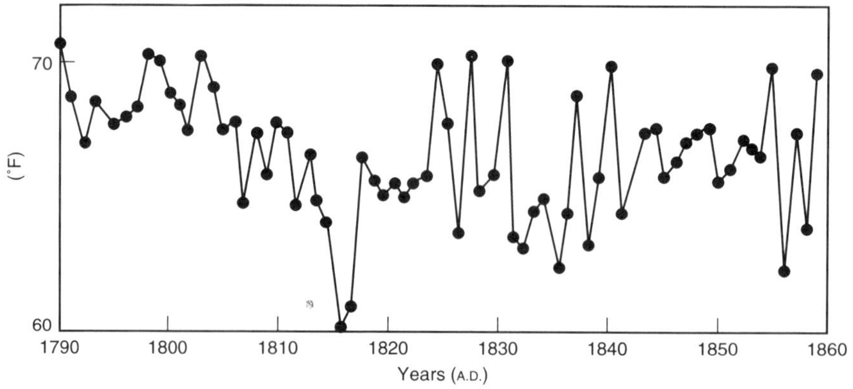

FIGURE 4–1 Temperatures for June in New Haven, Connecticut (as measured by presidents of Yale College) between 1790 and 1860 showing sharply lower values in 1816 and 1817. This drop in temperature is inferred to be due to the cooling effect on the atmosphere of the volcanic explosion of Tambora (Indonesia) in the winter of 1815.

TEMPERATURE VARIATIONS DURING THE CENOZOIC (THE PAST 65 MILLION YEARS)

Over the past 65 million years the remains of ancient life and recorders of the environment, both on the continents and in the oceans, have persisted so that they provide a good record of the changes in the global environment.

One such record is found in the accumulating sediments on the floors of the oceans. Ships, equipped with special coring tools or drilling rigs (Fig. 4–2), have traveled to every part of the oceans. Using their sampling devices, virtually continuous records of sediments have been recovered in cores. These cores often contain fossils of single-celled, calcium carbonate (Fig. 4–3) and silica (SiO_2) depositing organisms. Some of these organisms lived at the surface of the ocean and some at the bottom on the sediment floor. These "tests," as the hard parts of these organisms are called, carry a record, as a function of time, of the change in temperature of both the bottom of the ocean (at depths greater than 4000 meters) and the ocean surface.

The record is in a curious code that was deciphered after World War II, not by cryptographers but by geochemists implementing the methods of isotope fractionation, and using the element oxygen found in water (H_2O) and calcareous ($CaCO_3$) tests. The theoretical discovery that isotopes of an element could be separated by chemical and physical methods provided the basis for the enrichment of a fissionable isotope of uranium (^{235}U) and ultimately the atomic bomb. In principle, all isotopes of an element can be separated naturally

FIGURE 4–2 The drilling ship *RV Resolution* used in obtaining cores from the ocean floor. (Courtesy of the National Science Foundation.)

or artificially. Natural processes, however, affect only the lower atomic number elements from sulfur down to hydrogen.

Different molecules of a particular element each have different bonding characteristics. For a given type of molecule, say water (H_2O), these

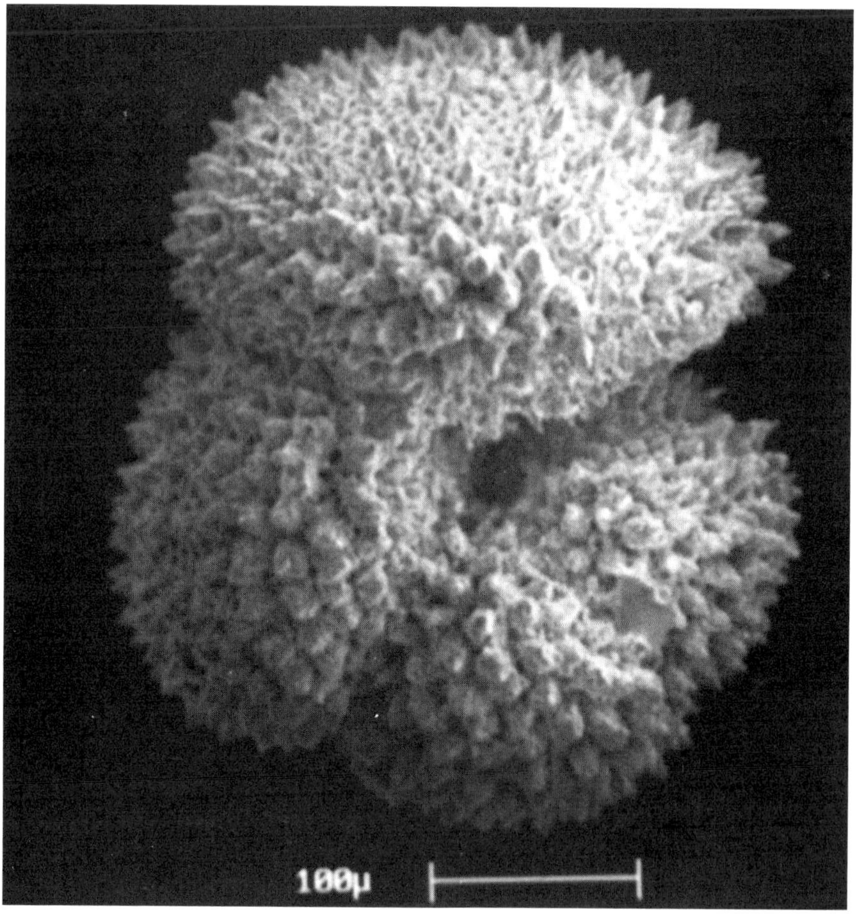

FIGURE 4–3 A typical foraminiferan test *(Globigerina bulloides)*. The test is made of calcium carbonate and is about 0.3 mm across. (Courtesy of G. A. Bartlett, Bedford Institute of Oceanography.)

bonding characteristics are slightly different for a molecule composed of the larger mass isotope (for our chosen example, ignoring hydrogen, $H_2{}^{18}O$) from the same type of molecule composed of the smaller mass isotope ($H_2{}^{16}O$). These molecules of water with different masses react differently under physical and chemical constraints. The "light" water as a gas (water vapor) diffuses faster than "heavy" water. The bonds holding "light" water in the molecule break more easily than the bonds in "heavy" water. The degree of difference in behaviors of the "heavy" and "light" molecules of water is sensitive to temperature. They are closer in behavior with higher temperature. The greatest disparity in behavior is at lower temperatures.

The breaking and reconstruction of bonds take place in chemical reactions. If, for example, water could exchange its oxygen atom with another molecule the rates of exchange of the "lighter" and "heavier" isotopes of oxygen would be different and also a function of temperature. In carbonated water (such as club soda) the oxygen in the dissolved CO_2 and the surrounding water exchanges until there are set amounts of ^{18}O relative to ^{16}O in the CO_2 and in the H_2O, determined by the bonding properties of each molecule type for each isotope. This distribution is a function of temperature. Carbonated water not only has dissolved carbon dioxide but also two ions formed by the chemical reaction of CO_2 and H_2O. These are called the bicarbonate ion (HCO_3^-) and the carbonate ion ($CO_3^=$). The formation of these ions comes from the simultaneous formation of hydrogen ions (H^+) to balance the electrical charge in the solution. As the hydrogen ion concentration increases we note it as an increase in acidity.

In most natural waters the presence of dissolved cations and their associated bases acts to lower the acidity of the solution but can also react with the carbonate ion to form precipitates when the concentrations of the ions exceed the solubility of the precipitating solid.

We write such an equation, controlling chemical precipitation, for calcium carbonate ($CaCO_3$) in the following manner:

$$Ca^{++}(aq) + CO_3^{=}(aq) = CaCO_3\ (s)$$

where (aq) and (s) refer to the dissolved state and the solid (precipitate) state, respectively. If solid $CaCO_3$ precipitate exists in the system then we express the equilibrium state when the rate of precipitation and the rate of solution of the precipitate are equal with a constant called the solubility product constant (written K_{sp}). The K_{sp} is related to the concentrations of calcium and carbonate ions in the solution. That is

$$K_{sp}(T) = [Ca^{++}] \times [CO_3^{=}]$$

where the brackets are used to designate concentrations.

It is generally true that K_{sp} is higher the warmer the solution, so that more precipitate will dissolve. That is the reason we write $K_{sp}(T)$ indicating that the value of K_{sp} is a function of the temperature.

A similar equation can be written for the exchange of oxygen isotopes between H_2O and $CO_3^=$, but its form depends on the exchange of oxygen isotopes. This equation is written as

$$H_2{}^{18}O + 1/3\ C^{16}O_3^{=} = H_2{}^{16}O + 1/3\ C^{18}O_3^{=}$$

and at equilibrium

$$K(T) = \frac{[H_2{}^{16}O][C^{18}O_3{}^{=}]^{1/3}}{[H_2{}^{18}O][C^{16}O_3{}^{=}]^{1/3}} = \frac{([C^{18}O_3{}^{=}]/[C^{16}O_3{}^{=}])^{1/3}}{([H_2{}^{18}O]/[H_2{}^{16}O])^{1/3}}$$

where *K(T)* is the isotope exchange equilibrium constant as a function of temperature.

We have knowledge of the isotopic composition of $CO_3{}^{=}$ by measuring it in a calcium carbonate precipitate. We can, in principle, measure the isotopic composition of the water also. The total number of oxygen atoms in water, however, is much greater than that found in the total carbonate ion dissolved in the water or precipitable as calcium carbonate, so that the deposition of $CaCO_3$ has an immeasurable effect on the isotopic composition of the water. Therefore the isotopic fractionation reflecting the temperature shows up only in the precipitated calcium carbonate and not in the water molecules. The displayed equilibrium reaction written above is actually determined from the study of the spectra of molecules and the application of quantum mechanical principles, but the fundamental behavior is thc same as our simplified representation.

In summary, two stable isotopes of oxygen, oxygen-16 (the commonest) and oxygen-18 (rarer) behave slightly differently when a $CaCO_3$ test is deposited from seawater and these differences are more pronounced at low temperatures than at high temperatures. By applying our theoretical knowledge of this relative behavior we can deduce a temperature for the oceans, top and bottom, by determining the oxygen-18 to oxygen-16 ratio, respectively, in planktic (surface dwelling) and benthic (bottom dwelling) organisms (specifically, the group of single-celled calcium carbonate depositors called *foraminifera,* or familiarly "forams"). The relationship between the oxygen-18/oxygen-16 ratio in a calcium carbonate test and the temperature of the water in which it grew is

$$t(°C) = 16.9 - 4.2\,(\delta^{18}O_c - \delta^{18}O_w) + 0.13\,(\delta^{18}O_c - \delta^{18}O_w)^2$$

where $\delta^{18}O_c$ is the parts per thousand difference in the $^{18}O/^{16}O$ of the foram test relative to a standard and $\delta^{18}O_w$ is the parts per thousand difference of seawater relative to the same standard. Relative to the oxygen in the water molecules composing seawater, the oxygen-18 to oxygen-16 ratio in this deposited calcium carbonate is larger the colder the water is from which it is deposited. The $\delta^{18}O_w$ value of contemporary seawater can be measured directly but it is more difficult to obtain the value for ancient seas. The reason is that the $\delta^{18}O_w$ is determined by the amount of water stored as ice on the continents since the snow precipitating at high latitudes is lower in $^{18}O/^{16}O$ than ocean water. At present about 15% of the water at Earth's surface is stored on Antarctica and Greenland. This storage results in a higher $\delta^{18}O_w$ in the contemporary ocean than it would be if the ice caps were not present.

What is the reason for this difference between the $^{18}O/^{16}O$ of high latitude snow and the ocean? Much of the water vapor in the atmosphere has its origin in the tropics, and the transport of water vapor from the equator to the poles is accompanied by progressive removal of the moisture from the air by atmospheric precipitation. Each step of removal of water as precipitation preferentially draws down the "heavy" water (enriched in ^{18}O relative to ^{16}O), leaving the remaining water vapor necessarily "lighter" as it is being transported to the poles. At the high latitudes water is precipitated as snow that is enriched in the remaining "light" water. The storage of "light" water in ice caps makes the main reservoir of water, the seas, "heavier" than it would have been without the presence of these ice caps. Major ice storage developed on Earth over the past 35 million years. By figuring the amount of lowering in $\delta^{18}O_w$ by the return of all the ice to the oceans prior to 35 million years ago, an estimate of the $\delta^{18}O_w$ of the ocean without the presence of polar ice caps and continental ice sheets can be made.

Figure 4–4 shows the $\delta^{18}O$ curve in benthic foraminifera over the past 65 million years inferred from results from the study of many deep-sea cores. Prior to about 35 million years ago, the $\delta^{18}O_c$–$\delta^{18}O_w$ is determined as described in the previous paragraph. It is evident that the temperature of the oceans was about 15°C warmer at the dawn of the Cenozoic than at present.

The ocean temperature ultimately regulates the general climatic patterns of the planet and the temperature on land. The study of the remains of ancient land plants over the past 65 million years indeed shows that relationship. Cooling of the land has been followed quantitatively by tracking the change in a special property of leaves of nonconiferous trees. It has been observed that in living plants virtually all nonconiferous trees in tropical environments have leaves that are smooth along the edges (Fig. 4–5). Proceeding poleward away from the tropics, as the mean temperature of the environment during the growing season diminishes, the number of tree species with *erose,* or serrated edges, such as maples or elms, increases relative to smooth-edged species. Consequently the proportion of species with erose leaves is a direct indicator of air temperature (Fig. 4–6). If we assume that temperature is the primary control on this pattern rather than length of day or precipitation, and is independent of evolutionary changes in species, then we can translate this information to the study of fossil leaf assemblages in strata covering a range of time periods. The results of such analyses indicate that over the past 65 million years, at a number of latitudes within the temperate zone, the trend has been toward lower mean temperatures as one progresses to the present (Fig. 4–7).

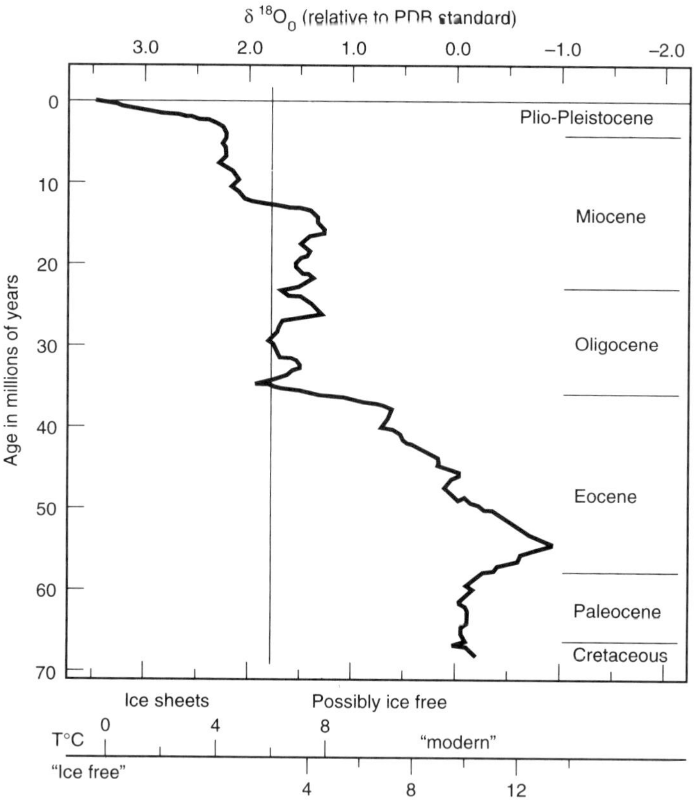

FIGURE 4–4 Composite curve of oxygen isotope data for Tertiary benthic foraminifera from the North Atlantic. The data can be transformed to ocean bottom temperature by setting the oxygen isotope composition of the ocean on an ice-free and ice-present (modern) basis. (From K. G. Miller, R. G. Fairbanks, and G. S. Mountain, 1987, *Paleoceanography,* v. 2, p. 1. Copyright by the American Geophysical Union.)

Why did the temperature of Earth decrease about 15°C over a 65-million-year period? The answer probably lies in the changes in the positions of the continents and oceans, the intensification of explosive volcanism, and the rise of high mountains first on Antarctica and then as the result of the convergence of India and China—all as the result of collisions and the openings of ocean passageways resulting from plate tectonics.

There is some evidence, although mainly inferential, that the carbon dioxide content of the atmosphere was also decreasing over the past 65 million years (see Chapter 7). If the decrease in CO_2 did occur, it would also probably be driven primarily by plate tectonics. The increase in glaciated mountains as

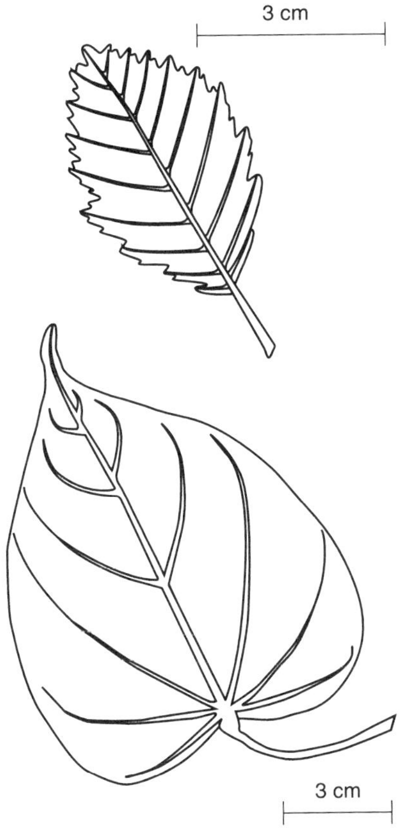

FIGURE 4–5 Degree of serration of leaves is related to temperature. The upper leaf is characteristic of plants in temperate climates and the lower smooth-edged leaf is typical of tropic plants. (After J. A. Wolfe, 1978, *Am. Sci.*, v. 66, p. 691.)

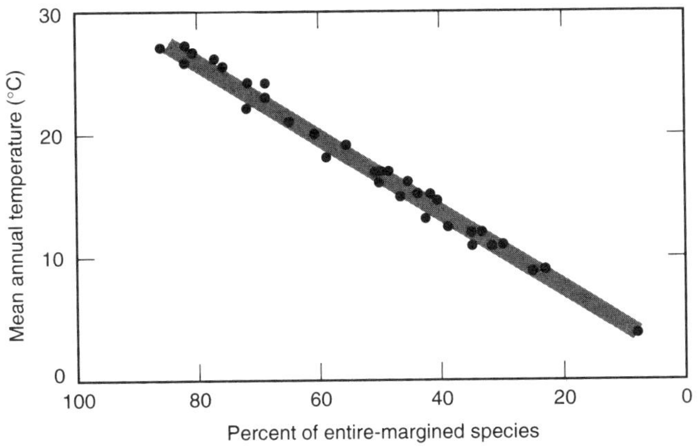

FIGURE 4–6 The proportion of entire-margined species is a direct reflection of the mean temperature. (After J. A. Wolfe, 1978, *Am. Sci.*, v. 66, p. 694.)

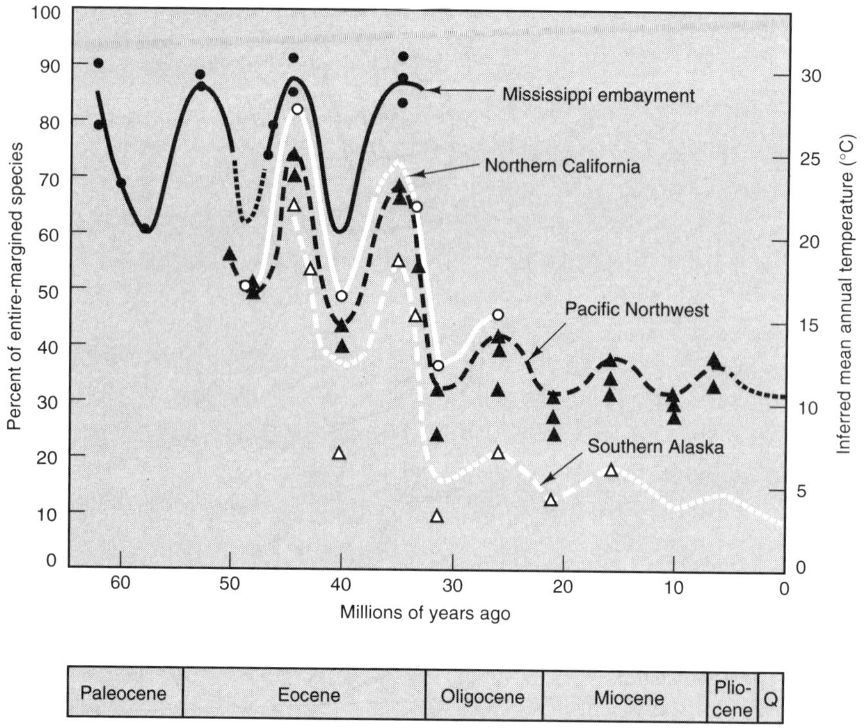

FIGURE 4–7 The percentage of entire-margined species in fossil plants shows a decrease in temperature from 65 million years ago to the present throughout North America. (After J. A. Wolfe, 1978, *Am. Sci.*, v. 66, p. 694.)

continental collisions occurred would increase the amount of pulverized "rock flour" which, as "glacial milk" draining ice fields, would act to absorb carbon dioxide from the air, as discussed in Chapter 3. The balance of carbon dioxide supply from the mantle and to the mantle also may have been changed. If the net atmospheric concentration of CO_2 decreased as a result of this process, the temperature of the atmosphere would decrease. Of course, as the temperature of the ocean surface dropped, reflecting the atmospheric temperature, the amount of water vapor in the air would also decrease, thus exacerbating the cooling trend.

CONTINENTAL GLACIATION IN THE LATE CENOZOIC

Valley glaciers were probably present on Antarctica as long ago as 50 million years, as evidenced by glacially transported fragments of rocks and minerals in sediments of that age found on the ocean floor around the continent. This small beginning in glaciation was followed by progressive increases of ice cover until a major ice cap of the kind we observe there today was fully emplaced about 15 million years ago.

As the plates moved on Earth following the much earlier break-up of Pangaea, the northern hemisphere gradually became the repository of most of the continents of Earth (Fig. 4–8). As the temperature of Earth's surface decreased, the elevated land areas of northern North America and Europe began to accumulate enough snow during winters to persist through the summers. The glaciers from the highlands flowed down and covered land at the lower elevations. The increase of snow cover and general decrease in global temperature led to the development of vast continental ice sheets about 2.5 million years ago. North America and Europe, at times, together contained twice the mass of ice now contained on Antarctica. The relict of the ice sheets of these expansive times of the northern hemisphere is seen today in the Greenland ice cap (or sheet), which contains about one twentieth of the ice of Antarctica.

As ice accumulates on the continents it creates a record of glaciation in the form of superficial, unconsolidated deposits only observable once the ice is gone. That recent unconsolidated sedimentary deposits throughout Europe and North America were the result of such a widespread glaciation in the recent past was not recognized until the middle of the nineteenth century. Before the identification of characteristic glacially induced features, these deposits were perceived to be relicts of the great flood recorded in the Bible associated with the story of Noah and the ark.

What are some of these indicators of glacial action? They can all be inferred from observations of the active valley glaciers in the Alps, Alaska,

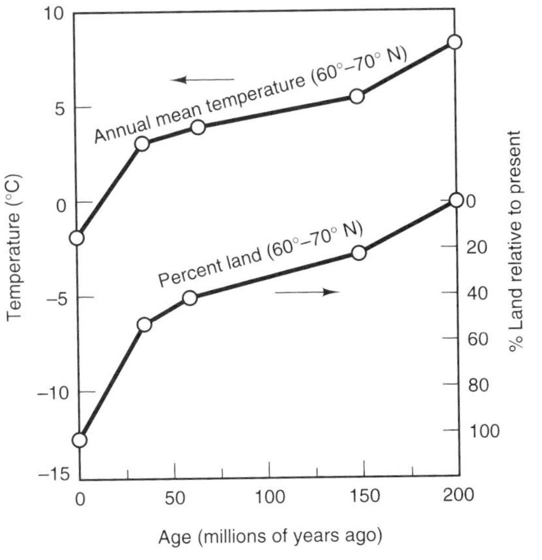

FIGURE 4–8 The percent of land at the latitudes around the Arctic Circle has increased since 200 million years ago and this increase has been greatest in the past 50 million years. The temperature of the region as well as the whole northern hemisphere also decreased on this time scale.

and elsewhere, and the continental ice sheets of Antarctica and Greenland. Among the most obvious are the following:

1. Striations are made on the channel bedrock along which a glacier moves. The striations are the result of the glacial ice dragging boulders and gravel along its path, thereby gouging the underlying rock surface with these abrasives.
2. Glacial polish is made by the same process but with very fine rock powder.
3. Large boulders and other deposits carried by the glacier responsible for the first two features are found near the terminus of the glacier where the rate of evaporation and melting ("ablation") exceeds the supply of new ice by flow. As ablation occurs at the glacier edge the glacially ground rocks accumulate and these deposits form a *terminal moraine*.
4. Random boulders and pulverized material are left along the path of the glacier when the final complete ablation of the ice has occurred.
5. Windblown deposits of very fine grained material are transported away from the glacial front. Some of these accumulations form cohesive deposits called *loess* (major farmlands in China and the state of Nebraska, for example, are on loess deposits).

When these features are found in the geological record they provide *prima facie* evidence that extensive glaciation occurred at that location in the past. Such large glaciations have been inferred for major continental areas not only in the recent past but also about 300 and 500 million years ago and probably many more times in the more remote past.

THE ICE AGES OF THE LAST 2.5 MILLION YEARS AS RECORDED IN DEEP-SEA DEPOSITS

On the basis of evidence in Europe and North America for the latest epoch of ice on the continents, we see a clear sequence of expansion followed by the virtual disappearance of the ice (by ablation, melting, and insufficient accumulation of new snow). It was not until studying deep-sea sediments, however, that the true nature of these advances and retreats of land glaciers were understood in a proper time frame. How is it possible to infer information about *continental* glaciations from *oceanic* deposits?

The answer lies in the study of the calcium carbonate deposits made by microscopic single-celled organisms, the foraminifera. It is true that the individual test carries an oxygen isotope record that can be related to the temperature of the ocean and the amount of continent ice storage, but each test also has a characteristic shape typical of each species. The different morphologies (Fig. 4–9) found in an assemblage of tests provide a record of oceanic environmental conditions. The assemblage of organisms is characteristic of oceanic parameters such as temperature (Fig. 4–10), but salinity and the concentrations of the nutrients necessary for the sustenance of life are also factors.

If we core the sediments accumulating at the bottom of the ocean we can obtain a time series of foraminiferal assemblages. If major changes in the temperature of the oceans (or other environmental parameters) occurred over time then the assemblage of foraminiferal species, represented by the different morphologies of their tests, would be different following the pattern shown in Figure 4–10. By this process of logical reconstruction of the past with the aid of dating techniques based on radioactivity, the sequence of changes, primarily in the temperature of the oceans, at various locations as a function of time can be inferred.

It was discovered that at some locations, such as the equatorial regions, the change in foraminiferal assemblage recorded a warm temperature with little variation in time whereas at higher latitudes, especially in the North Atlantic, the changes were dramatic (Fig. 4–11). These changes were inferred to be the oceanic indicators of the ice age variations recorded in deposits on land. The correlation was precisely made for the past 40,000 years by radiocarbon dating of the marine calcium carbonate tests in oceanic deposits, and the organic carbon of continental vegetation on land associated with glacial deposits.

With this focus on ocean deposits as the continuous and global recorders of the variations in the extent of continental glaciation on the planet, the exploitation of the marine record for reconstructing the climatic cycle of the past millions of years or so was possible. Climate information gleaned from the morphology of forams, combined with oxygen isotope data on these tests, allows us to reconstruct the climate history of the Late Cenozoic, or the Pleistocene, as this time of rapid change in continental glaciation is called.

As we have seen in the previous section, the oxygen-18 to oxygen-16 ratio ($\delta^{18}O_c$) in a foram test gets higher the colder the water is from which it precipitates, assuming that the oxygen isotopic composition remains virtually constant. Seawater itself can show variations in the oxygen-18 to oxygen-16 ratio ($\delta^{18}O_w$) depending on the amount of ice in ice caps and continental ice since such precipitation is enriched in the light isotope over

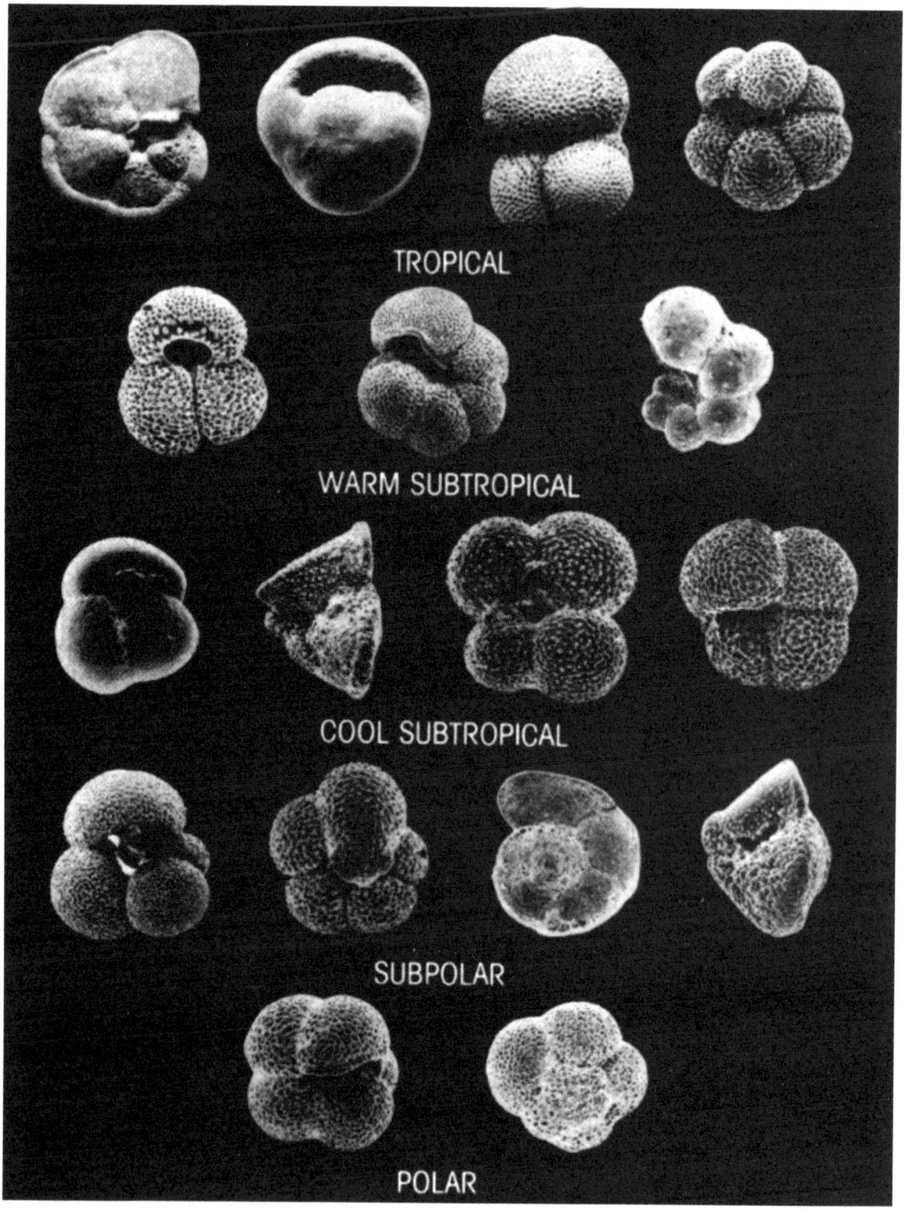

FIGURE 4–9 Distribution of some modern species of planktic foraminifera. (From J. Kennett, 1982, *Marine Geology*, Prentice Hall.)

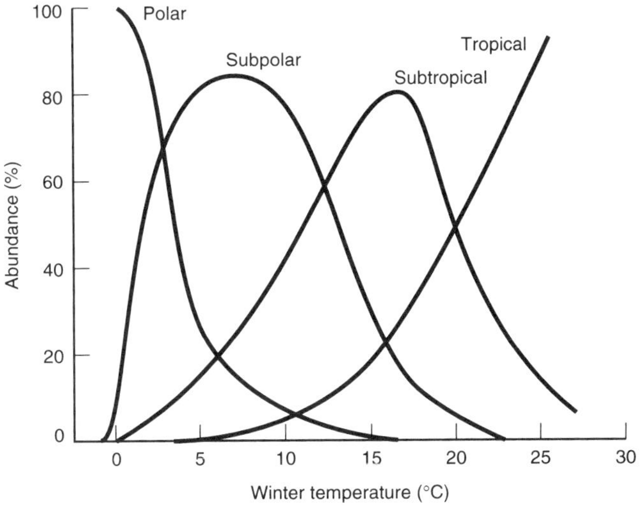

FIGURE 4–10 General abundance trends for four assemblages related to winter surface temperature. (After J. Imbrie and N. G. Kipp, 1971, p. 71 in *Late Cenozoic Glacial Ages*, ed. K. K. Turekian, Yale University Press.)

the heavy one. Hence if there is more "light" ice on the continents, the remaining ocean water becomes a little saltier and, so far as the oxygen isotopes in water are concerned, more enriched in oxygen-18 relative to oxygen-16. The remarkable fact is that when climate is more frigid and the ocean temperature responds to this global cooling, the ice on continents also increases. As a result of this increased ice storage and the lowered ocean temperature, the oxygen-18 to oxygen-16 ratio in the foram tests are higher. Therefore the oxygen isotope signature of a foram test provides the strongest evidence for the degree of continental glaciation and the associated climatic effects (Fig. 4–12).

THE LINKAGE OF THE CYCLES OF GLACIATION WITH EARTH'S ORBITAL BEHAVIOR

The time series of $\delta^{18}O_c$ values shown in Figure 4–12 is not random but has periodicities that can be deciphered by proper analytical techniques such as those used in wave analysis. When such an analysis is made, the $\delta^{18}O_c$ pattern can be resolved into its component wavelengths with three periods: 100,000 years, 40,000 years, and 20,000 years. What is the physical significance of these periods?

The answer to this question may be found in our understanding of the way heat is distributed on the surface of Earth as the result of its orbital

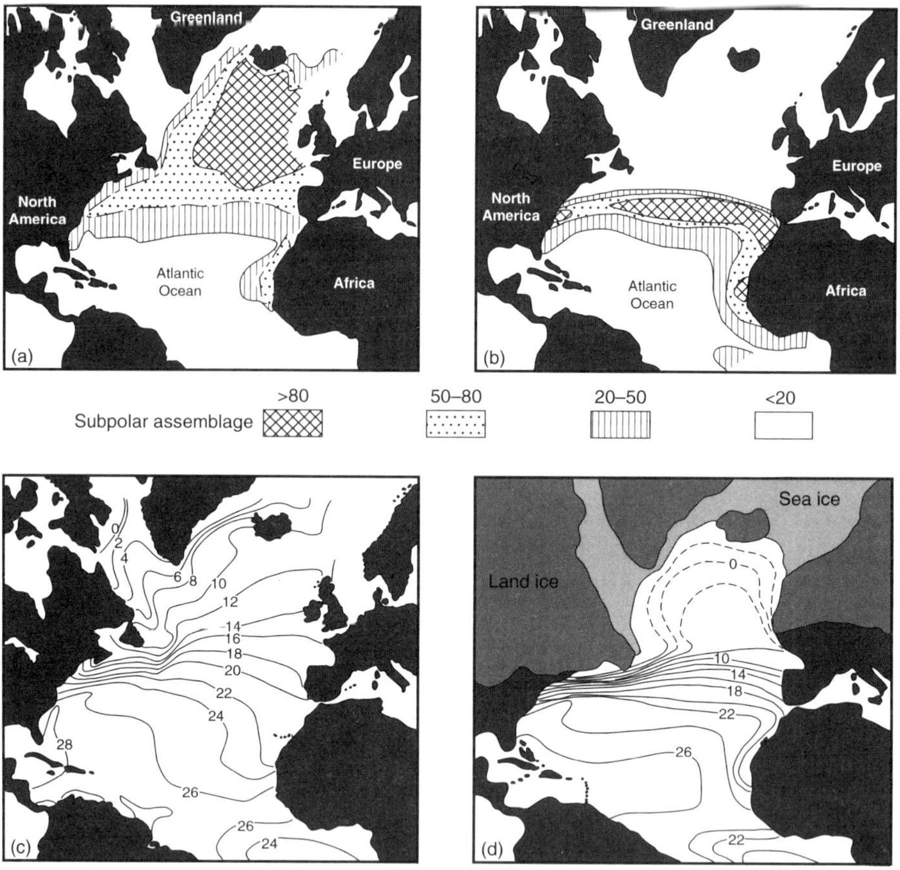

FIGURE 4–11 The observed distribution of foraminifera in core top ("contemporary") sediments (a) in the Atlantic, and those at the peak of the last glaciation (18,000 years before present) (b) as expressed by the subpolar cluster of Figure 4–10. The observed present-day summer ocean surface temperature distribution (c) and the summer ocean surface temperature distribution (d) inferred for the peak of the last glaciation from the foraminiferal distribution patterns are shown. (After N. Kipp and A. McIntyre et al., 1976, *Geol. Soc. Am. Mem.* 145, CLIMAP project.)

behavior. Earth's axis is tilted 23.5° from the perpendicular to the plane described by Earth's orbit around the sun ("the plane of the ecliptic"). The tilt of Earth is the cause for our seasons. In the northern hemisphere summer the north pole tilts toward the sun giving us the summer solstice (about June 21), which is the maximum radiation of the year at the surface. The opposite effect occurs in the northern hemisphere winter when the north pole points

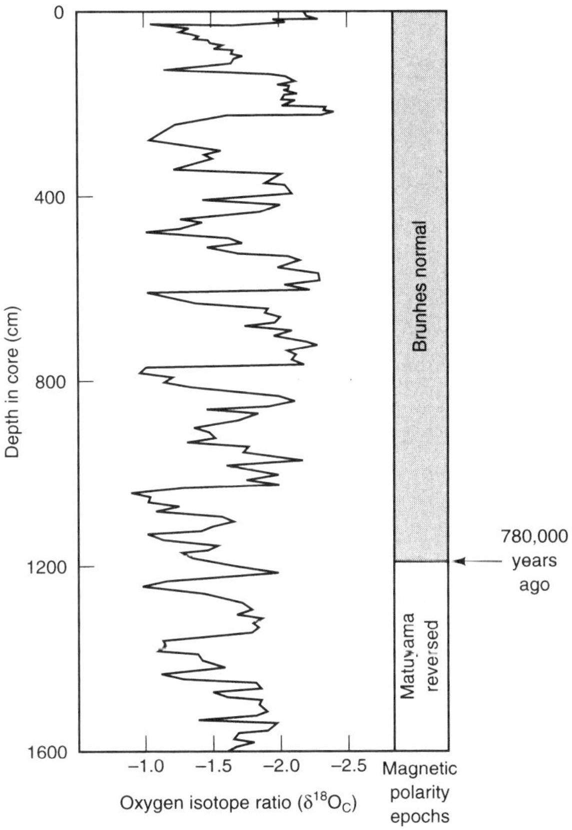

FIGURE 4–12 Planktic oxygen isotope and magnetic reversal stratigraphy of a Pacific deep-sea core. The variations in the oxygen isotope ratio (expressed as variations relative to a standard) indicate changing climatic conditions reflected in the oceans. The more positive (or heavier) the $\delta^{18}O$ value, the colder the climate. (Data from N. J. Shackleton and N. D. Opdyke, 1973, *Quaternary Res.*, v. 3, p. 39.)

away from the sun. The north rotational pole during the year, at the present time, always points toward the Pole Star (Polaris). Earth, as as well as the other planets, describes an elliptical orbit around the sun with the sun at one of the foci of the ellipse (Fig. 4–13).

These orbital parameters, however, are not fixed over time but rather change in a systematic fashion driven primarily by the gravitational pull of the sun on a tilted planet as it revolves in its orbit. A Serbian scientist, M. Milankovitch, worked out the variation of these orbital forcings in 1914 while detained as a political prisoner. The ellipticity changes with time.

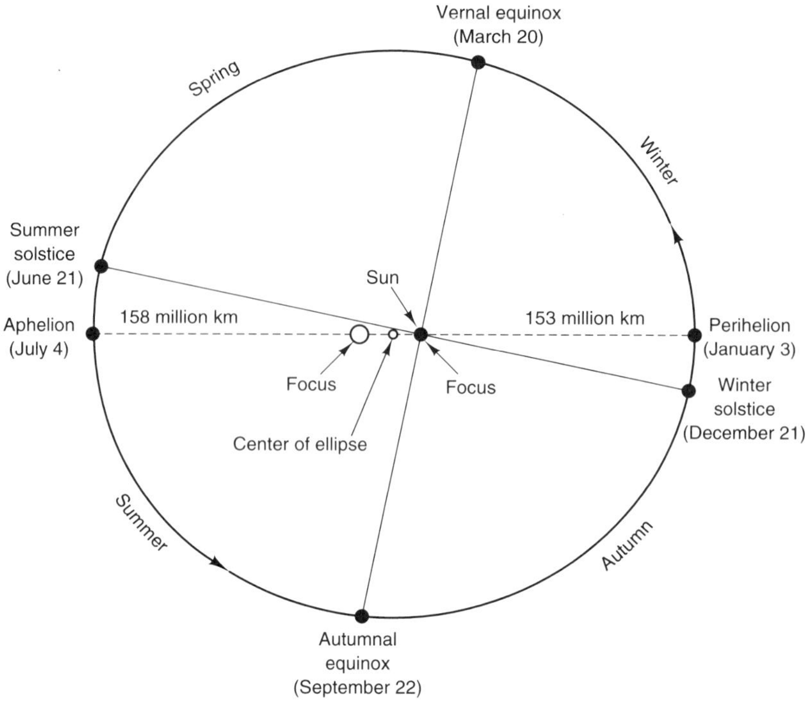

FIGURE 4–13 Earth describes an elliptical orbit with the sun at one of the foci, the tilt of Earth at 23.5°, and each pole constantly pointing to the same spot in the field of stars (that is, Polaris, the North Star), results in the seasons and not the distance from the sun. At the equinoxes, the day and night are of equal length all over the globe. At the summer solstice, the North Pole is tipped in the direction of the sun, and the northern hemisphere has the longest day of the year. At the winter solstice, the North Pole is tipped away from the sun, and the northern hemisphere has the shortest day of the year.

This change from a more circular to a more oblong ellipse takes place over a 100,000 year period. The departure from a circular orbit is called the planet's *eccentricity*. In addition, although in any one year the poles of Earth point to definite locations in space, sometimes identified by a star like the Pole Star (Polaris) in the north, Earth actually behaves like a wobbling top and the orientation of the pole actually describes a circle pointing to different parts of the celestial sphere over a time scale of about 20,000 years. This change in orientation is called the *precession of the equinoxes*. A third variable in the orbital parameter is the *tilt* of Earth's axis over time. This tilt changes by about 1° above and below the present-day value of 23.5° with a period of

40,000 years. These three cycles of eccentricity, precession of the equinoxes, and the tilt of Earth's axis act to influence the amount of heat delivered to different parts of Earth seasonally and over longer periods of time.

These orbital time periods match the cycles of 20,000, 40,000, and 100,000 making up the main components of the wiggles of the $\delta^{18}O_c$ data. It is a natural conclusion, therefore, to couple climatic change to the orbital forcing. Milankovitch specifically calculated the amount of heat reaching the northern hemisphere in the summers in response to the three forcing parameters. He argued that if the amount of heat reaching the northern hemisphere in the summer was lower in some years than other years, the possibility of accumulating and retaining snow packs over the summer during times of low summer radiation would permit the development of sustained continental ice sheets. Cooler summers in the northern hemisphere based on the orbital effects would be balanced by warmer winters, and this warming would cause more evaporation from the oceans and therefore more precipitation at higher latitudes. The increased precipitation of snow would enhance the growth of the ice sheets. The reverse would happen during the other part of the cycle, namely ice sheets would diminish in size.

Although the relationship between the climatic record in deep-sea cores and calculated orbital parameters is strong, and the explanation involving heat flux and continental ice sheet growth is reasonable, the exact replication of the behavior of ice sheets, such as their sudden end and occasional episodic regrowth and decay, as occurred 10,600 years ago, is not yet obvious. Clearly, other effects such as the geography of oceans and continents and the variability of the sun's energy output or Earth's albedo are also important controls on the changing climate of the ice ages. There are other periodic controls in the way the sun's heat affects Earth. These include the periodic encounters with dust left by passing comets. The nature and location of these clouds together with periodic changes in Earth's orbit may enhance the Milankovitch effects. Nevertheless, the "pacemaker" quality of orbital forcing undoubtedly is an important part of the variation of climate over the past 2.5 million years.

It can be argued that the entire development and dispersion of humans took place under the climatic variations of the last 2.5 million years. Humans and their ancestors may not have always encountered ice sheets but the decrease in worldwide air temperatures by as much as 5°C at the peaks of glaciation must have had an environmental influence on migrations. Humans have always been subject to changes in climate, and part of the general adaptability of modern humans to the wide range of climates on Earth must be due to a continuing accommodation to these changing conditions imbedded in us through natural selection.

TEMPERATURE CHANGES OVER THE PAST 11,000 YEARS

The history of modern humans effectively began at the end of the last ice age about 11,000 years ago. (The period of time from 11,000 years ago to the present is called the Holocene.) Within a short span of time after the end of the last glaciation, the temperature of Earth increased, the ice disappeared from Europe and North America except in valley glaciers of the high mountains, and, as we shall see in Chapter 6, sea level rose 120 meters. Our present geography and climate are the consequences of these massive changes resulting from the warming of the planet.

There have been additional changes in the temperature at Earth's surface since the major transformation from a glacial to an interglacial regime. About 5000 years ago there was a period of increased warming around Earth recorded in pollen records and other indicators. During medieval times there was also a general warming, at least as recorded by Europeans. Starting about 1300 A.D. the climate began to deteriorate dramatically. This deterioration was markedly so in the lands surrounding the North Atlantic Ocean. Vikings who had settled on Greenland vanished by the end of the fifteenth century and the year 1695 A.D. was the coldest year modern Europeans had ever experienced. The canals of the low countries were frozen solid—drastically affecting the shipping industry of Rotterdam and other ports. The fiercely cold winters had devastating effects on the health of people in the Germanic states. This nadir in climatic conditions was followed by a slow, although not monotonic, increase in temperature until the middle of the nineteenth century. Several pronounced dips in temperature, including the winter experienced at Valley Forge that almost undermined the American Revolution, occurred during this time. It is no wonder that the period from 1300 A.D. to 1820 A.D. has been called the "Little Ice Age." During this period, the drop in worldwide temperatures relative to the preceding Middle Ages may have been about 1.5°C (Fig. 4–14).

What was the cause of this deterioration in climate? There is circumstantial evidence that the change in the heat output from the sun might have been the responsible agent. A record of the heat output of the sun may be found in the study of "sunspots." Sunspots are relatively dark spots observed on the sun by Galileo, who first measured their number in 1610 A.D., and since then by other astronomers who have continued these observations. The average length of time between the peaks of sunspot numbers is 11 years, but the amplitude of the sunspot frequency curve is not constant. A strong correlation between the number of sunspots on the face of the sun and the temperature record of the period under consideration exists. The reason for this correlation remains obscure.

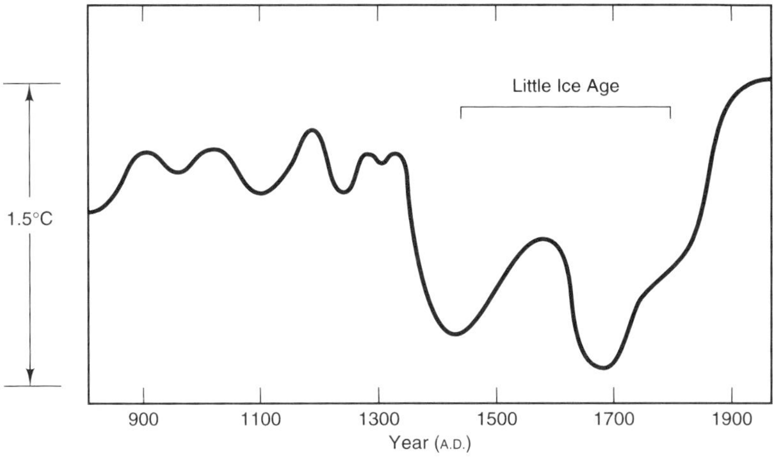

FIGURE 4–14 Climate of the past 1000 years. The graph is an estimate of winter conditions in Eastern Europe, as compiled from manuscript records. During the Little Ice Age (1450-1850 A.D.), mountain glaciers all over the world advanced considerably beyond their present limits. (Adapted from H. H. Lamb, 1969, by J. Imbrie and K. P. Imbrie, 1979, *Ice Ages*, Enslow Publishers.)

Although warming has generally occurred from about 1700 A.D. to the present, since 1870 it has been at a more accelerated pace than any time since the Little Ice Age ended (Fig. 4–15). The increase in temperature is correlated with increased fossil fuel burning. There has been an increase in the carbon dioxide content of the atmosphere from about 300 parts per million by volume (ppmv) to about 360 ppmv from 1870 through 1993. It is not surprising that many people feel that there is a relationship between the two patterns. The difficulty in making a simple correlation is that although the CO_2 in the atmosphere has been increasing continuously since 1870, the trend of the temperature of the planet's surface has actually had reversals, most markedly in the two decades betweem 1940 and 1960 (Fig. 4–15).

Yet the role of CO_2 as a greenhouse gas cannot be ignored, and its influence on the temperature of the atmosphere eventually must be observed. Recently, the detailed analysis of temperature records from around the globe has shown that before 1960 the variations in global temperature could be accommodated as being the result of natural variations, but after 1960 there might be a reasonable correlation of temperature increase with human-caused increases in CO_2.

In summary, we have seen that the temperature at Earth's surface has not been constant. Starting 65 million years ago with a surface temperature about 15°C higher than it is today, with a smaller gradient in temperature

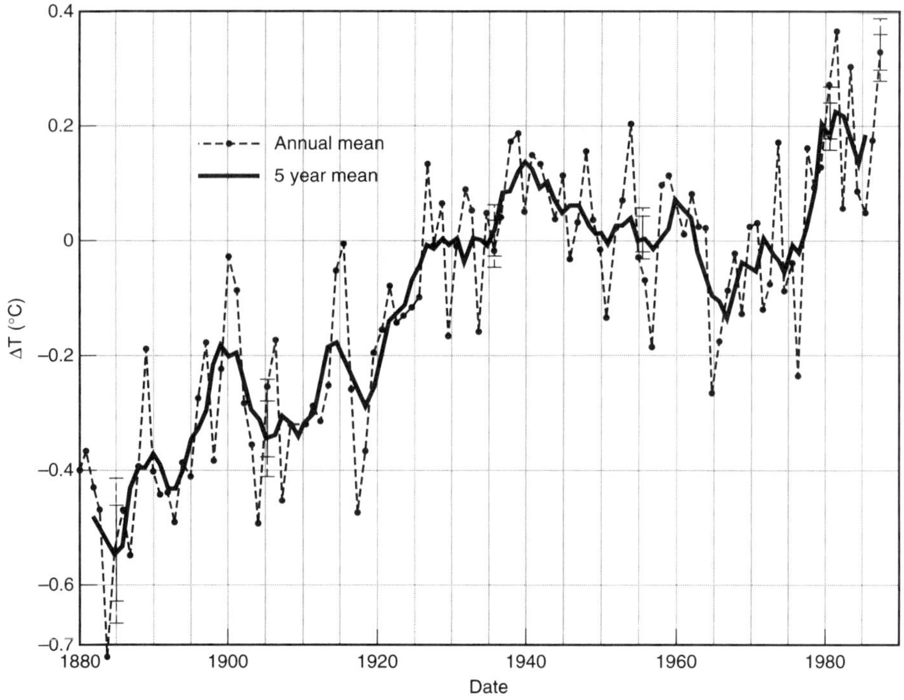

FIGURE 4–15 The change of global temperature over the past 110 years. (Compiled by NOAA and NASA investigators.)

from pole to equator, Earth gradually cooled and became more strongly temperature zoned across latitudes. This zonation ultimately caused the development of an ice cap covering all of the Antarctic continent by 15 million years ago, and 2.5 million years ago caused the beginning of a cycle of glaciation and deglaciation in the northern hemisphere. The fluctuation in temperatures was about 5°C through this frequently repeated cycle. The causes for the initiation of this pattern of changes can be understood in terms of the location of continents and oceans, the formation of mountains, and maintenance by the properties of Earth in its orbit around the sun.

The fluctuations in temperature may also be in response to changes in the solar energy output. The temperature fluctuations observed in the Holocene may in part be due to these changes. Since 1870, the combination of solar effects and the increase in the greenhouse gas carbon dioxide, as the result of burning fossil fuels, may have caused the fastest increase in global temperature since the end of the Little Ice Age.

PROBLEM:

Oxygen isotope paleothermometry depends on the distribution of the oxygen isotopes between calcium carbonate tests of marine organisms and seawater. Theoretical and experimental results show that with increasing temperature this difference decreases so that if the isotopic composition of the ocean reservoir remains effectively constant, a shell (or test) will have an increasingly higher $^{18}O/^{16}O$ ratio as the temperature at the time of precipitation (shell growth) decreases.

All measurements of oxygen isotopes in paleothermometry are made on carbon dioxide gas released from the shell by acid. The ambient seawater value can be measured on the same scale by measuring the value of carbon dioxide equilibrated with seawater. All measurements are made relative to a standard (which by agreement has generally been a Cretaceous belemnite from the Peedee Formation in South Carolina, called PDB) and expressed as $\delta^{18}O$, where

$$\delta^{18}O = \left[\frac{\left(^{18}O/^{16}O\right)\text{sample}}{\left(^{18}O/^{16}O\right)\text{standard}} - 1\right] \times 1000$$

and represents parts per million difference from the standard.

A. The following set of data relates temperature of shell (or test) deposition to the oxygen isotope composition of the shell (or test).

t(°C)	$\delta^{18}O_c$
30°	– 3.14
25°	– 1.98
20°	– 0.81
15°	+ 0.35
10°	+ 1.51
5°	+ 2.67
0°	+ 3.84

1. Graph the relationship.
2. From the graph determine the constants ***a*** and ***b*** in the straight line equation having the form

$$t(°C) = a + b\,\delta^{18}O_c$$

where $\delta^{18}O_c$ refers to the measured value of the test.

B. The above equation assumes that the seawater value ($\delta^{18}O_w$) on the same scale is zero. Actually, the complete equation should be

$$t(°C) = a + b\,(\delta^{18}O_c - \delta^{18}O_w)$$

1. Assume that for the past 11,000 years $\delta^{18}O_w$ has been 0.00 and from 11,000 years B.P. (Before Present) to 22,000 years B.P. $\delta^{18}O_w$ was +2.00

from independent evidence (such as ice core data and glacial history). If a core raised from the ocean bottom showed that planktic foraminifera over the past 22,000 years have a constant $\delta^{18}O_c$ value, how did the temperature of the surface oceans change 11,000 years ago?

2. If you assumed that the ocean before and after 11,000 years B.P. had $\delta^{18}O_w = 0.00$, what would the change in temperature of surface ocean water appear to be?

3. If the deep, ocean bottom temperature near a low latitude site at present is 1°C and surface ocean temperature is 20°C and the $\delta^{18}O_w = 0.00$, what would be the difference in $\delta^{18}O_c$ of a benthic and planktic foraminifera test, for example, $(\delta^{18}O_c)_{deep} - (\delta^{18}O_c)_{surface}$? Under what condition would this difference be maintained if the $\delta^{18}O_w$ were +2.00, that is the value of the 11,000 to 22,000 year B.P. ocean of question 1?

5

THE CIRCULATION OF THE ATMOSPHERE AND OCEANS

The atmosphere and the oceans are both fluids. The absorption and release of heat from the sun drives the movement of each of these fluids on Earth. The oceans and the atmosphere are in intimate contact and influence each other's behavior. The oceans, with their large reservoir of heat, tend to control the temperature of the air. The winds, on the other hand, control the circulation of the surface oceans. Both the atmosphere and the oceans respond to the differences in heat delivery from the sun seasonally and with latitude.

As fluids, the atmosphere and oceans show patterns of turbulence on a variety of scales. In the atmosphere the large-scale patterns of weather are observed daily from satellites as cloud movements. In the oceans the complexity of the surface currents occurs on a longer time scale but can still be observed from satellites. The meandering and the formation of eddies in the Gulf Stream can be followed for weeks by monitoring ocean surface temperature. There are large-scale circulation patterns in both the oceans and the atmosphere, driven ultimately by the way in which heat is delivered across the planet's surface and the way the rotating planet acts to influence the behavior of fluids in motion. The atmosphere not only transfers heat from one part of Earth to the other by this motion but water vapor as well. The transportion of this water vapor affects the precipitation distribution on the land, the development of ice caps, and the salinity of the oceans.

THE CIRCULATION OF THE ATMOSPHERE

The heat per unit area delivered from the sun is not evenly distributed on Earth's surface. Because Earth is a sphere, heating is highest at low latitudes and lowest at the poles (Fig. 5–1). The distribution of heat on the surface also changes with seasons as the result of the tilt of Earth's axis. The higher heat at low latitudes relative to the poles results in the transfer of heat toward the poles primarily by the convection of the atmosphere, although ocean currents also play a role. The net effect is that the loss of heat from Earth is almost the same at all latitudes (Fig. 5–1).

This transfer of heat is the consequence of atmospheric convection on a rotating planet subject to gravitational constraints. Hot air, being less dense than cold air, rises at the equator (the "doldrums") and, on cooling, descends around 30° (N or S) latitude (the "horse" latitudes). This general circulation was recognized by sailors because the doldrums and horse latitudes resulted in a minimum in the horizontal component of wind. Samuel Coleridge's Ancient Mariner exclaimed: "Day after day we stuck nor breath nor motion, as idle as a painted ship upon a painted ocean." The recognition that the air movements at these two latitudes were part of a large convective cell was made by G. Hadley in the middle of the eighteenth century and therefore is called the Hadley cell (Fig. 5–2). Although he was concerned with explain-

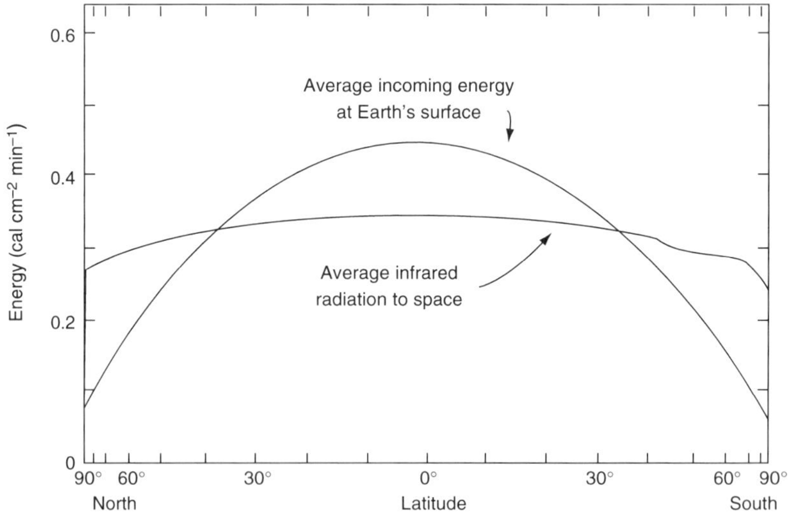

FIGURE 5–1 About four times as much solar energy reaches Earth's surface at the equator as at the poles, but radiation of energy to space is nearly the same everywhere on Earth.

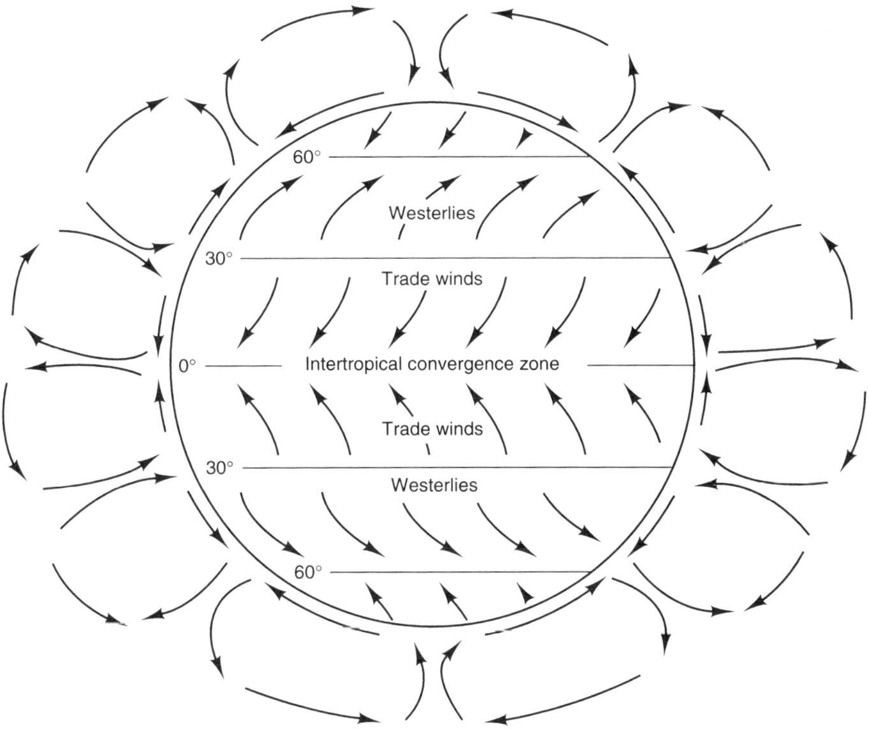

FIGURE 5–2 Convection of the atmosphere and the prevailing wind fields of Earth. The rise of air at the equator and descent at 30° latitude was recognized by G. Hadley as responsible for the still air at the doldrums (equator) and the horse latitudes (30°). Since then the general atmospheric circulation has been divided into three Hadley-like cells.

ing the behavior of the air between 0° and 30° latitude, his insight into the controls of the behavior of the atmosphere can be extended to global circulation. Generally, three such circulation cells from the equator to each pole have been identified to explain the large-scale convective regime needed to transfer heat from the equator to the poles.

We now consider the behavior of the air as it descends at 30° latitude. The direction of tropospheric winds is predominantly westerly (wind blowing from the west) between 30° and 50° and predominantly easterly (wind blowing from the east) between 30° and the equator. The "neutral" latitudes are the doldrums and the horse latitudes, as described. The tangential or linear velocity of Earth varies with latitude, being fastest at the equator and slowest at the poles. The air descending at the horse latitudes has the velocity characteristic of the tangential or linear velocity of the planet's surface at that latitude. As the air descends it must move north or south of the line of descent: It moves in part toward the pole and in part toward the equator (Fig. 5–2). As it moves toward the pole the air is moving faster from west to east than solid Earth, resulting in the westerlies. The air moving toward the equator is moving slower than the ground resulting in the easterlies. These tendencies are reinforced by another property of Earth's rotation, as we shall see.

Wind direction also was obviously of great concern to the sailing ships of the past involved in transoceanic travel. As interest was high in efficiently moving from the "Old World" across the Atlantic to the "New World," the easterlies, called the "trade winds," were of paramount importance. Sailing under the westerlies was assisted, as we shall see, by a strong northward- and eastward-moving oceanic current, the Gulf Stream. As most airplane travel today occurs in air lanes between 30° and 50° latitudes we see the expression of the westerlies at high altitudes (~10 kilometers) as a strongly coherent band of fast-moving air traveling from west to east that is called the "jet stream." The direction and strength of the jet stream account for flight times that are generally shorter going from west to east than the opposite.

Earth is rotating on its axis and as a result there appears to be a movement of the field of stars making up the night sky. Actually it is our rotation in the universal frame of reference that gives us this illusion. According to Newton's first law, a body set in motion anywhere in the universe will move in a straight line at a constant velocity unless acted on by an external force. A baseball thrown by a pitcher can never speed up but actually must slow down as the result of the friction of the air. It also falls to Earth rather than heading for the stars because of the force of Earth's gravity. Both of these are external forces that act on the baseball after it leaves the pitcher's hand.

Yet on a larger scale, the inertial behavior of a body set in motion on a rotating planet must be viewed within the universal framework. That is, when a body on Earth is set in motion it will move in a straight line relative to the universal framework stars, whereas at the same time Earth is rotating on its axis. Thus relative to Earthly frame of reference, the path of the moving body actually is seen to be curved. The moving object is not breaking Newton's law but rather obeying it in the universal frame of reference. As the path of the moving body is deflected from a straight line on Earth (after correcting for gravity and any atmospheric frictional effects) it has the appearance of being affected by a force acting at right angles to the direction of motion. This fact was recognized by G. G. Coriolis in the nineteenth century. In the northern hemisphere, as one looks at Earth from the North Pole it appears as a rotating disc. This Earth "disc" rotates counterclockwise. For this reason an object set in motion in the northern hemisphere will be deflected, relative to terrestrial geographic frame of reference, to the *right* because of the Coriolis force. In the southern hemisphere the deflection will be to the *left*.

In our simplified model of circulation based on the Hadley cell and tangential (or linear) velocity differences with latitude, we assumed an ascent and descent along defined latitudes. Weather maps never look so simple but appear to be a series of pockets of descending air (high pressure areas) and ascending air (low pressure areas). If a "plume" of air rises it draws from the surrounding air. As air rushes in toward the plume it is deflected by the Coriolis force so that the sum total of the air pattern surrounding the low pressure area resembles a gyre or a cyclone with air moving counterclockwise. As a plume of air descends (high pressure), the added air disperses radially, again deflected by the Coriolis force to result in a clockwise anticyclonic pattern (Fig. 5–3).

THE CIRCULATION OF THE OCEANS

The Coriolis force operates on the oceans as well as the air. The ocean surface warms in response to the heat it receives from the sun but, because water has a high heat capacity, the rise and fall of its temperature as the result of heating and cooling proceeds slowly. Therefore surface currents can transport warm water from the equator poleward to a significant degree and thereby influence the local air temperature beyond the effects of direct heating of the atmosphere by the sun's rays. The transfer of warm waters to high latitudes in the North Atlantic results in the warming of the United Kingdom

FIGURE 5–3 A high pressure system is due to air subsiding from above and flowing in a clockwise fashion at the surface. A low pressure system is due to air rising from the ground surface as the result of heating. As air is drawn up from the surface, a counterclockwise path is followed. The high pressure and low pressure patterns are due to the Coriolis effect.

and Ireland beyond what direct heating of the air above these lands by the sun would allow in the wintertime.

The surface ocean currents, however, are driven directly by the wind and the effects of Earth's rotation. Winds act on the ocean surface causing waves. The surface water is put in motion and without the Coriolis effect this motion would be in the direction of the wind force. Because of the Coriolis force, however, the surface layer of the ocean in the northern hemisphere is deflected slightly to the right of the direction of the wind. The movement of the surface water causes the next deeper water layer also to move in the direction enforced on it by the movement of the surface layer. As the movement of the surface layer is to the right of the wind direction, so the next layer moves to the right of the surface ocean layer which is forcing the deeper water to move. This process continues to deeper and deeper layers, until the weakness of the force effectively prevents further coupling. The profile of water movement direction and strengths is called the Ekman Spiral (Fig. 5–4) after V. W. Ekman, its formulator. The net result of the Ekman Spiral is that the mass of a thickness of surface ocean water effectively moves, on average, in a direction at right angles to the direction of the wind.

Consider the northern hemisphere of the Atlantic Ocean. The prevailing westerlies and easterlies blowing across the ocean cause surface water to "pile up" in the Sargasso Sea as the result of the Coriolis force acting on the surface ocean layer and its resulting Ekman Spiral (Fig. 5–5). As water piles up it flows downhill as the result of gravity. This flow results in the development of a gigantic oceanwide clockwise gyre. The current is intensified on the western side of the ocean because of Earth's rotation. As this water has come from a tropical zone where heating of the surface ocean is the most intense, the intensified boundary current transports warm water northward at a high velocity in a narrow ribbon we call the Gulf Stream. All currents, deep and shallow, have western boundary intensifications because of the rotation of the planet.

At high latitudes the radiative loss to space of heat, supplied by warm surface currents, especially during the long winter night, results in the warming of the air and cooling of the water. The resulting cold, salty, dense water sinks. Around Antarctica intense chilling of the Southern Ocean (as the ocean around Antarctica is called) results from the melting of very cold ice flowing from the Antarctic ice cap. This process of cooling chills the water sufficiently so that, despite dilution with fresh water from the melting glacial ice, the resulting water is the densest of the waters of the oceans and sinks to the deepest layer. The deep circulation of the oceans depends on differences in the stratification according to differences in density resulting from differences in temperature and salinity

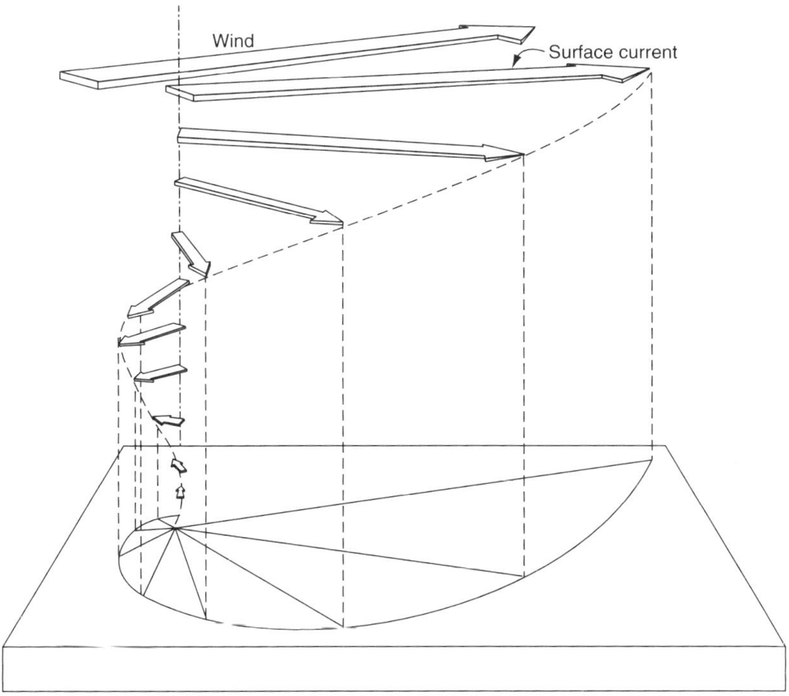

FIGURE 5–4 Schematic representation of the Ekman Spiral shows the response of the ocean column to winds. Each layer of the water affects the next deeper layer according to the deflection expected from the Coriolis effect. A wind-driven current in deep water (rather than coastal shallow waters) moves, on average, at right angles to the direction of the wind.

resulting from chilling, warming, precipitation, melting, and evaporation; the movement of water to accommodate the differences in density due to temperature and salinity differences is called *thermohaline* circulation. The major features of this deep circulation are shown in Figure 5–6.

The sinking of deep, dense water implies that existing water in the ocean is displaced as the newly formed water spreads away from the point of formation. This transport requires that water move from depth to the surface not only to accommodate the newly formed deep water but also to supply water to the high latitudes from which water is extracted for deep water formation by heat loss and the associated cooling. The general process of upward motion of water is called upwelling. Based on radiocarbon dating of ocean water profiles and through the use of other chronometers, the mean velocity of upwelling throughout the oceans is known to be about 4 meters per year. As the mean depth of the oceans is about 4000 meters, the average

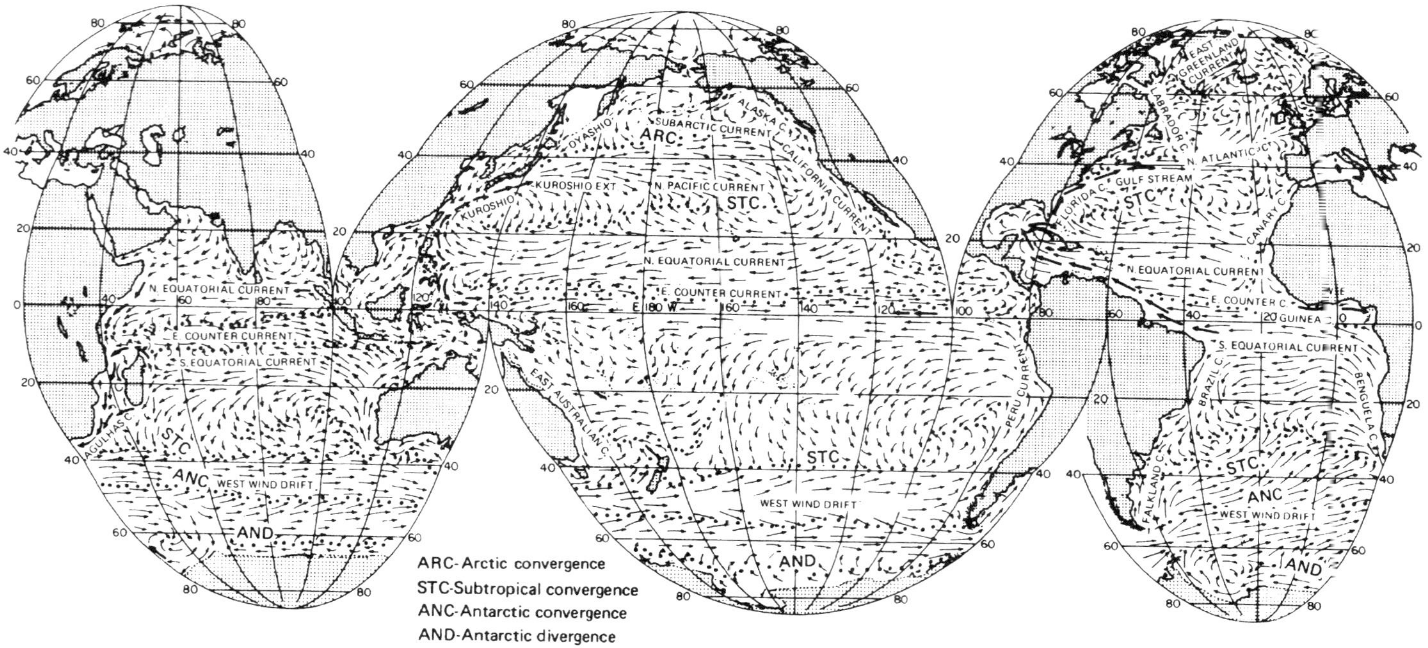

FIGURE 5–5 Ocean-surface currents in February–March. (After H. V. Sverdrup, M. W. Johnson, and R. H. Fleming, 1942, *The Oceans*, Prentice Hall.)

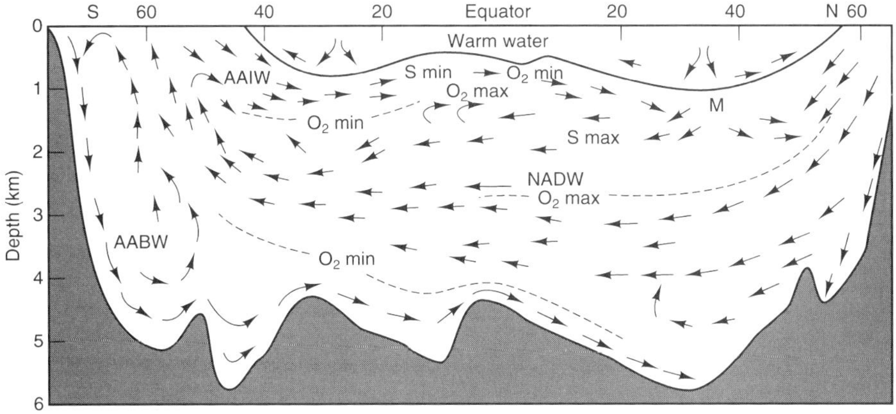

FIGURE 5–6 The thermohaline circulation in the Atlantic Ocean. AAIW = Antarctic Intermediate Water; AABW = Antarctic Bottom Water; NADW = North Atlantic Deep Water; M = Mediterranean Water. (After G. Neumann and W.J. Pierson, Jr., 1966, *Principles of Physical Oceanography*, Prentice Hall.)

time of upwelling of a parcel of water from the bottom of the ocean to the surface is 1000 years.

Upwelling occurs most intensely on the eastern parts of the ocean basins and along the equator. As described above, the piling up of water in the center of each of the hemispheric basins of the oceans, with the subsequent development of strong western boundary currents, depletes surface water at the equator and the eastern boundaries. In order to compensate for the loss of surface water, deep water upwelling occurs.

Surface waters, if not supplied by upwelling deep water, will soon become unproductive as the available phosphate and nitrate necessary for life are used and biological particles are transported by settling to the deeper parts of the ocean basin. In deep water the nutrient elements, phosphorus and nitrogen, are regenerated so that a pattern of low nutrient element concentration at the surface and high concentration at depth is maintained. At the site of upwelling, nutrient-rich waters are supplied to the surface where sunlight leads to photosynthesis and biological productivity (Fig. 5–7). Changes in the intensity of upwelling will obviously cause changes in the biological productivity of a region.

INTERANNUAL CLIMATIC CHANGES DRIVEN BY COUPLED OCEAN-ATMOSPHERE CIRCULATION

The seasons define the major climatic features of different areas of our planet. For many regions, there is commonly a hot period and a cold period,

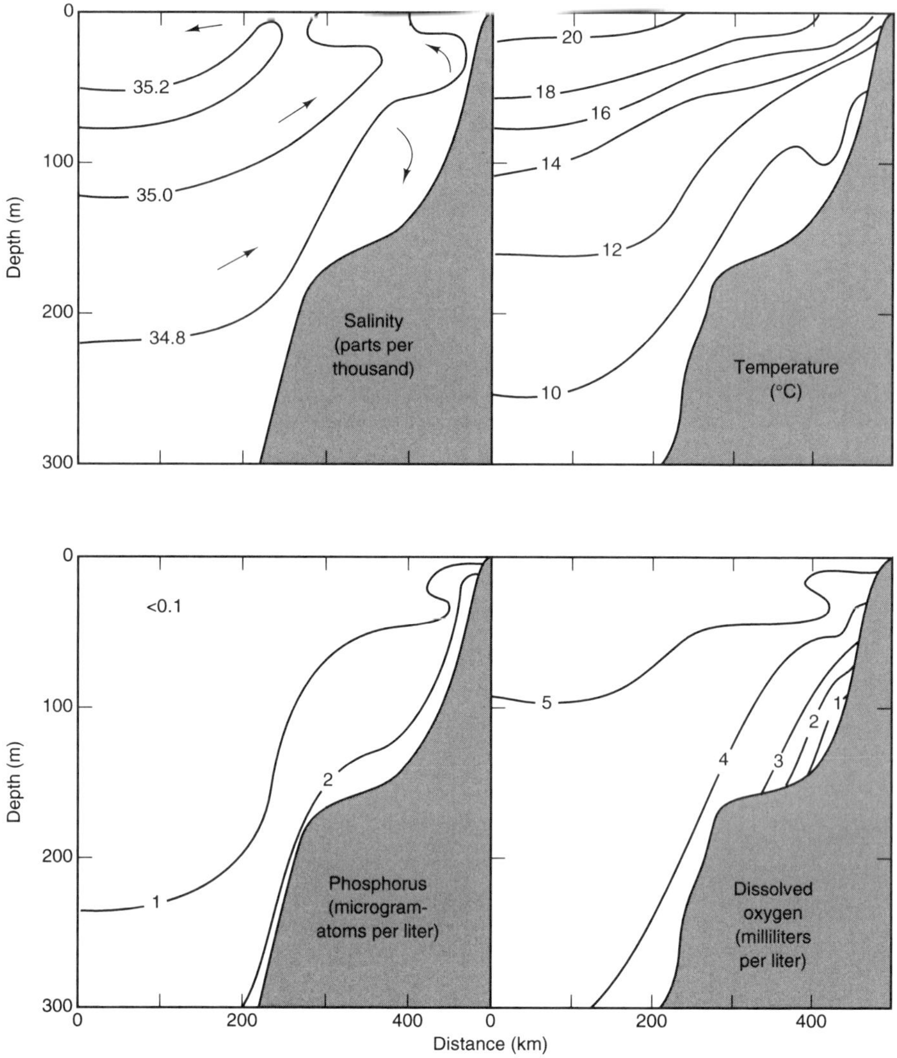

FIGURE 5–7 Schematic representation of water properties in an area of wind-induced upwelling. Note that the upwelled water comes from a depth of about 200 meters. (After G. Gross, 1993, *Oceanography*, Prentice Hall.)

a wet period and a dry period. The general qualities of temperature, humidity, types and frequency of precipitation, and direction and strength of winds together define the climate of a region. Although climate is dominated by seasonal components, climatic changes may also occur interannually. The so-called 100 year floods, such as experienced in 1993 in Arizona, or the approximately 3 year changes in the Pacific called El Niño (see below) indicate that the climate of a region, on long time scales, can be highly variable. Only with an understanding of these natural cycles can we try to identify or predict changes that might be induced by human activity.

The Monsoons

India and other south Asian countries experience a strong seasonal alteration of climate called the monsoons (from the Arabic word for "season"). The winter months are marked by dry winds traveling from the northeast, and the summer months are marked by strong, warm rains from the southwest. The consequences of this seasonal change are drought in southern Asia during the winter and poor fishing off the southern flank of the Arabian peninsula and Somalia on the one hand, and torrential rains for the summer months in India and the other countries of the region and strong upwelling off Arabia and Somalia leading to improved fishing.

One cause for this marked change in climatic behavior is the fact that there is more solar energy delivered during the summer than in the winter, but that in itself would not lead to the extremes of the monsoons without two other features of the region. The first is the sustained warm surface waters of the equatorial Indian Ocean, and the second is the high elevation of the Himalayas and the Tibetan Plateau in general. The combination of solar flux, the elevation of these great mountains, and the warmth of the equatorial ocean to the south leads to the monsoons of today. How does this coupling work?

During the winter months the Himalayas are at their coldest. The air above this great frozen and elevated land is strongly cooled and descends primarily to the southwest toward the equator. As it makes its way to sea level it is warmed but it lacks moisture—resulting in a drought-like situation along the path. The sea represents a warm surface where the air above is less dense than the cooler air arriving from the mountain trajectory, and this difference sustains the strong northeasterly winds. In summer the sparse air atop the Himalayas and the surrounding terrain is warmed by the increased radiation. Actually, the air on land is warmer than the air above the surrounding ocean which is maintained at a more nearly constant temperature all year long. The hot air rises and is replaced by high-humidity, lower temperature air from the ocean, dominantly from the southwest. As these water-saturated southwesterly winds reach land and are elevated by the topography, the stored moisture in the air condenses, resulting in the torrential rainfalls of the summer monsoon (Fig. 5–8).

The existence of this exaggerated shift in climate in southern Asia and northern Africa depends on the existence of the Himalayas. Without the

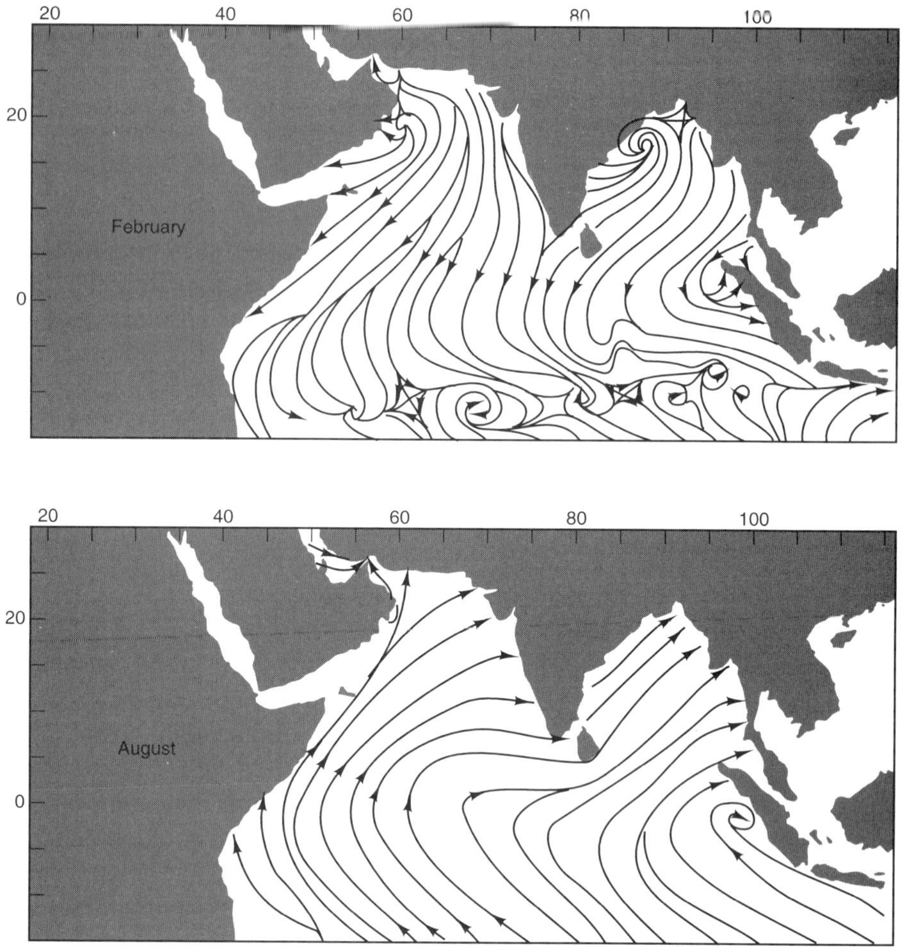

FIGURE 5–8 The monsoon winds of the Indian Ocean change direction between February and August.

existence of these mountains, the monsoons would be greatly attenuated. Based on geologic evidence, the Himalayas started coming into being after the India plate began pushing into the Asia plate about 50 million years ago. The actual development of the Himalayas with the associated Tibetan Plateau started about 17 million years ago and may have reached the present elevation about 7 million years ago.

Have the Asian and northern African monsoons maintained the same strength once the Himalayas were formed? The answer is no, since the solar flux is the driving base. As was discussed in Chapter 4, the solar flux in the northern hemisphere summer is subject to variation because of orbital changes. As this flux is an important control on the forces that drive the winds, the strength of the monsoons can be expected to vary proportionally to the summer solar flux. If we refer to the earlier discussion of the orbital controls acting to regulate the growth and decay of ice sheets, we note that one of these parameters, the precession of the equinoxes with an approximately 20,000-year cycle, also has the ability to influence the monsoonal intensity in Asia and northern Africa because it determines the radiant flux in the northern hemisphere summer (Fig. 5–9). At the present time Earth in its orbit is farthest from the sun during the summer of the northern hemisphere in its precession cycle, whereas 10,000 years ago it was the closest to the sun during the northern hemisphere summer.

The higher heat during the summer about 10,000 years ago caused the Asian and northern African monsoons to be stronger than they are today, thereby bringing more rain throughout the region during the summer months. The evidence for this high summer precipitation exists in the lushness of vegetation, the increased tropical fauna, extensive human settlements, large rivers, and higher lake levels found throughout the Sahara Desert—determined from archaeological and satellite studies. Radar beaming from Earth-orbiting satellites penetrates dry sand and the returned echoes show the terrain hidden by the sand drifts. This picture of a buried geography reveals ancient river valleys and human settlements.

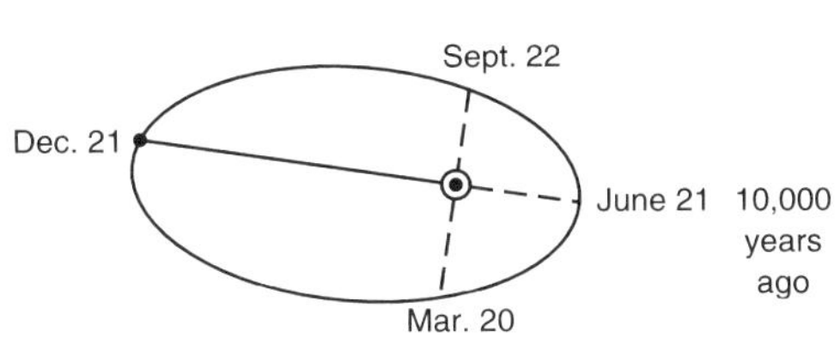

FIGURE 5–9 The precession of the equinoxes results in a change in the time of year in which the equinoxes occur. At present these occur on March 20 (Spring) and September 22 (Fall). The dates of the solstices are June 21 and December 21. The equinoxes and the solstices shift slowly around the Earth's elliptical orbit, and complete one full cycle about every 20,000 years. Ten thousand years ago, the winter solstice occurred at the long axis of the orbit most distant from the sun. Today, the winter solstice occurs at the short axis of the orbit closest to the sun. (After J. Imbrie and K. P. Imbrie, 1979, *Ice Ages*, Enslow Publishers.)

Since about 10,000 years ago the strength of the monsoons has been decreasing as the solar flux in the summer to the northern hemisphere has been decreasing. The aridity of the Sahara and southwestern Asia attests to this severe change. The expansion of aridity in the Sahel has been inevitable although it certainly has been exacerbated by the actions of humans. The desperate acts of survival by the Sahel region tribes have depleted the sparse vegetation and expanded the desert southward from the edge of the Sahara beyond the normal expansion.

El Niño and the Southern Oscillation

An important oceanic phenomenon occurs in the equatorial South Pacific which has dramatic climatic consequences not only for South America but also for much of the rest of the world. Indeed it was the discovery of the fluctuating strength of the Indian monsoons that led to the discovery of the worldwide nature of this phenomenon. At approximately 3-year intervals the great surface pool of warm equatorial water in the Pacific spreads eastward instead of journeying to the west as it normally does (Fig. 5–10). When this event occurs, generally around Christmas time (therefore "El Niño" or "the Boy Child": referring to the Nativity), the warm surface water approaches the coast of Peru, inhibiting the upwelling of cold nutrient-rich waters almost completely. The consequence of El Niño is virtual elimination of anchovy fishery. The absence of anchovies causes massive diminishing of the sea bird population feeding on them. Predatory fishes, such as tuna, are dislocated so that fisheries are in general depleted. Torrential rains occur along the coast and deeper into the interior as the result of the warm waters.

When El Niño occurs the increased temperature of the water close to the eastern boundaries of the Pacific causes increased storminess along the coast as far north as most of the state of California. Some meteorologists believe that the warm pool of water affects the climate throughout North America—making the Gulf and East Coasts warmer and generally wetter during the winter than in the years when El Niño is not present. The western Pacific waters are generally cooler during El Niño resulting in decreased rainfall in Australia causing drought and natural and human-initiated, large-scale biomass burning. Any modification of the surface water temperature in the western Pacific and adjacent Indian Oceans will affect the temperature gradient and water content of the air involved in the monsoons of Asia and northern Africa. Those years when El Niño has been intense have also been marked by weak monsoonal rains the following summer. The surface waters in the eastern Indian Ocean are cooler than normal, resulting in smaller concentrations of water

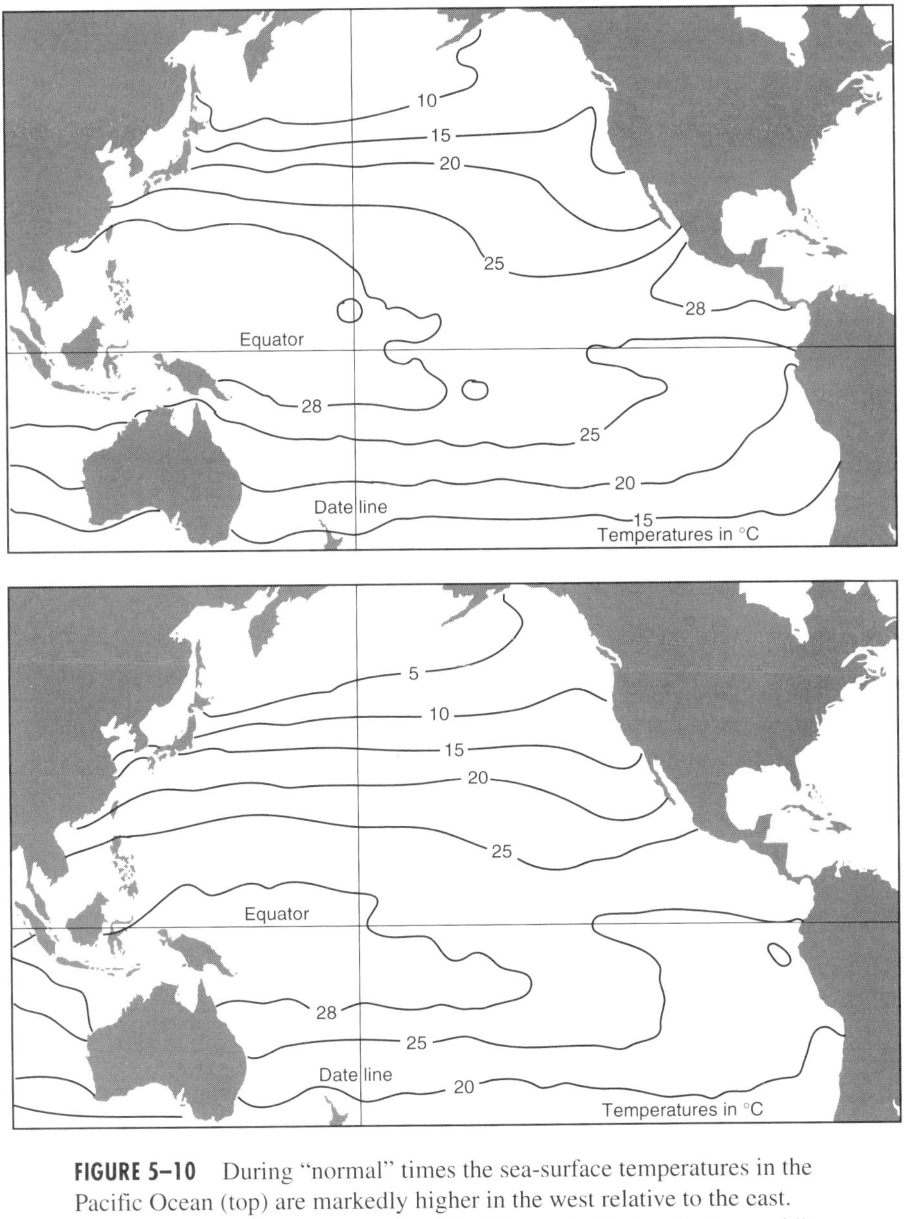

FIGURE 5–10 During "normal" times the sea-surface temperatures in the Pacific Ocean (top) are markedly higher in the west relative to the east. Temperatures in the western tropical Pacific are the highest in the world's oceans, whereas those in the eastern Pacific are the lowest found at such latitudes. When warm surface ocean temperatures spread to the east (bottom), a warming occurs along the South American coast. This warming commonly first appears around the beginning of the year, close to Christmas, therefore it is called El Niño. (After E. M. Rasmusson, NOAA.)

vapor in the air making its way around the Himalayas. "Failed" monsoons take a tremendous toll on lives in India as the monsoons provide water needed for agriculture. The absence of El Niño has been presumed to be the "normal", condition. The approximately 3-year cycle of El Niño occurrences coupled with oscillations in the sea-surface temperature of the South Pacific is called the "Southern Oscillation."

Obviously, strong changes in climate occur on time scales that are not part of the yearly seasonal cycle. Although the most striking is the El Niño–Southern Oscillation ("ENSO") of the warm surface ocean pool of the Pacific, other changes in the temperature distribution of the surface oceans also modify local climates. A small change in conditions at one part of Earth can have consequences for other remote areas through the complex behavior of the atmosphere in motion. For this reason the climate for any year or even season is not predictable, despite what the *Farmer's Almanac* says, and the local weather forecasters have hopes for a modest degree of reliability for at most about three days.

PROBLEM:

The ocean circulates more slowly than the atmosphere. One way to determine how long water resides at great depth before reaching the surface is to use the changes in the natural $^{14}C/^{12}C$ between surface values and deep water. The values for $^{14}C/^{12}C$ in the Pacific Ocean, expressed relative to the prebomb atmospheric value, are

depth	$(^{14}C/^{12}C)/(^{14}C/^{12}C)_{atm}$
surface	0.995
deep	0.970

A. What is the nominal "age" of surface ocean carbon relative to atmospheric carbon dioxide?

B. What is the "age" of deep ocean water relative to surface ocean water?

C. If the average depth of the ocean is 4 km, what is the average rate of upwelling of the oceans, assuming that transport of deep water to the surface is through vertical advective movement?

6

SEA LEVEL

The stability of sea level is a serious concern for people living along the coasts. During storms severe shifts in sea level pose danger. The relative rise in sea level as the result of the sinking of the land, in certain areas like the Gulf Coast, causes coastal dwellers to be concerned for property and livelihood—if not for life itself. Great stories of the power of the sea like the Noahic flood of the Bible have sparked our imaginations and challenged our understanding of the coastal oceans.

We are concerned about sea-level changes on a variety of time scales. The best way to address the questions of future risks due to sea level change is to understand the range and time scales of past and ongoing changes.

TIDAL CYCLES

For those living along the coast the periodic rise and fall of the sea is an important fact of the local environment. We call this phenomenon the tidal cycle. Knowledge of the period and amplitude of the tidal cycle is required for maritime ventures. Oceanic tides are the result of the gravitational forces exerted by the moon and sun on Earth. The amplitude of the tidal cycles is not the same everywhere but is determined by the local basin configuration and the alignments of the moon, sun, and Earth. The tidal cycles in the Mediterranean and Caribbean Seas have very small amplitudes, whereas parts of the English Channel, areas in North America, and the Bay of Fundy have twice-daily tidal maxima of as much as 50 feet (~15 meters) relative to the minima. At all locations the largest amplitude occurs when the moon, sun, and Earth are lined up (full moon and new moon). The approximately twice-daily ebb and flow of the tides is described as the semidiurnal tidal cycle. In some places there is only one high tide and one low tide a day and this situation is therefore described as a diurnal tide cycle. In addition to the periodic tide, occasional large local fluctuations in sea level relative to the coastline occur. These episodic changes, observed in certain parts of the world, are called *tsunamis* and they are caused by large waves made by earthquakes, massive volcanic eruptions, and large slumps of terrain along the ocean margins. Their amplitudes are often so large that, when they occur in populated areas, at first they expose the bottoms of harbors and then inundate their coastal cities almost without warning.

MEASURING SEA-LEVEL CHANGES REGIONALLY

Changes in sea level are experienced at coastal sites that are beyond these tidal or episodic time scales. The causes of these changes are diverse. Some changes and the forces causing them are regional and some are worldwide. Over the past century in North America and parts of Europe tide gauge records show local long-term changes in sea level beyond the rhythmic tidal changes (Fig. 6–1). These records indicate rises in sea level (relative to land to which the gauge is fixed) at some sites and drops in sea level at others. Where sea level is rising, accumulating marine deposits such as salt marshes can be useful monitors of the rise.

In places where tide gauge data show that sea level is dropping relative to land, such as in California and Alaska, there are also evidences of wave-carved features high above the present shoreline, indicating a long history of uplift of the coastline. The uplift of the land is associated with the convergence of tectonic plates. In other regions, sea level is rising relative to the land at a rapid rate. This accelerated coastal submergence is due to the extensive anthropogenic pumping of groundwater without a compensating recharging of the groundwater reservoir. Other areas show fluctuations of sea level, both higher and lower, over historical times that can be ascribed to local warps in the land due to regional geologic causes such as the growth and decline of volcanic activity.

In addition to the mentioned forces acting to give variable local sea-level change from place to place, the deglaciation of the continents about 11,000 years ago also has had a significant effect on sea level. Earth, as a rotating solid with some plasticity, will seek to maintain the same amount of mass per unit area at the surface to the center of Earth along any given latitude.

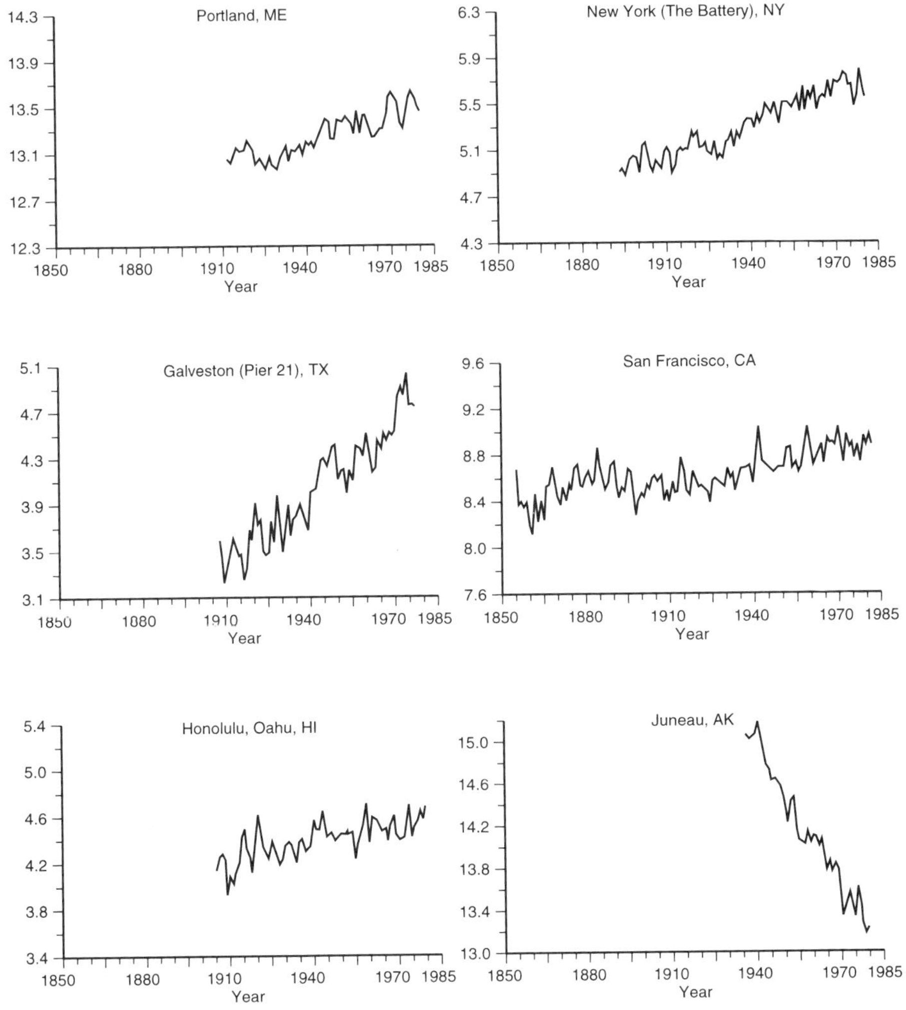

FIGURE 6–1 Tide gauge data for selected sites in the United States showing the changes in the yearly mean sea level.

This tendency is called *isostasy.* When ice covered the continents, the upper mantle behaved plastically and flowed radially away from the region of increased mass due to the addition of ice. The flow of the mantle acts to compensate the loss of mass under the oceans resulting from the transfer of water to the glaciers. There is a delay in the process because Earth's mantle has a high viscosity relative to water. When the ice melted in a short time scale, there was then a deficiency in mass at that site and the mantle began to flow back to compensate. Since this flow in a viscous mantle does not occur immediately, there is still a distortion seen in the surface topography resulting in either a "rebounding" land surface standing above a prior strandline or a downward warping because of the flow of the mantle to the region where melting of glacial ice caused a sharp departure from isostatic equilibrium. Obviously the determination of how much of a change in sea level observed locally is due to relative changes in the elevation of the land and how much is due to a worldwide increase in ocean level is not an easy thing to determine. Attempts, however, have been made to determine such a curve and one such effort is shown in Figure 6–2. The worldwide rise in sea level over the past 100 years, by these calculations, is less than 20 cm.

CAUSES OF WORLDWIDE SEA-LEVEL CHANGE

The most obvious change in worldwide sea level is the consequence of continental ice storage as implied in the preceding chapter. For example, if all the Antarctic and Greenland ice caps (see Table 3–2 on page 52) should melt, the amount of water in the ocean basins would increase and sea level would rise

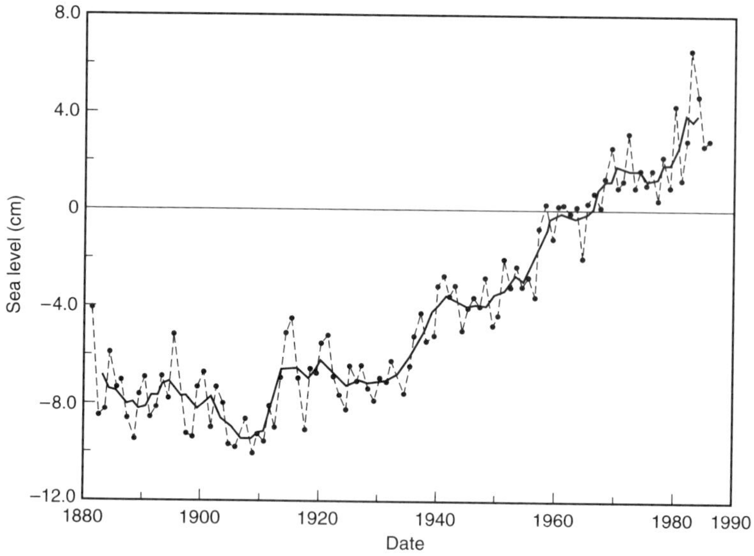

FIGURE 6–2 Global mean sea-level rise over the last century. The baseline is obtained by setting the average for the period 1951–1970 to zero. The dashed line represents the annual mean, and the solid line the 5-year running mean. (From T. P. Barnett, 1988, National Climate Program, NOAA. Reproduced in *Climate Change*, 1990, Report of IPCC Working Group 1, Cambridge University Press.)

by about 60 meters (200 feet). When the last large North American and European continental ice sheets developed starting about 70,000 years ago, water was extracted from the ocean and worldwide the sea dropped to a lower level than it is today. Therefore one way to lower sea level worldwide is to transfer water from the sea to continental ice sheets both at the poles and on the northern hemisphere continents. On the other side, the melting of some or all of this ice will result in a worldwide rise in sea level.

A smaller increase in sea level can result from the expansion of seawater as the oceans warm up. As the oceans were on average about 15°C warmer about 65 million years ago, this expansion also would contribute to the increase of sea level, already high at that time because of the absence of continental ice sheets.

In addition to the fluctuation of ice on the continents and the expansion (or contraction) of the oceans, one other factor enters into the fluctuation of sea level on the long time scale. This factor is plate tectonics. If we assume that the surface area of Earth is invariant over a specified time period (say, hundreds of millions of years) and during that time period the ratio of the area of continental crust and ocean basins has remained effectively constant, and the volume of seawater is fixed, then any changes in the average depth of the ocean basins will obviously affect sea level. What water the ocean basins cannot accommodate must lap on to the continents, thus effectively changing sea level so far as any continental datum is concerned.

Let us consider the sequence of events involving the continents and oceans once Pangaea, the megacontinent, began to split apart about 200 million years ago. The splitting between the Americas and Europe-Africa took place along what we now call the Mid-Atlantic Ridge. Since then the American continents have been moving away from the European and African continents at the rate of about 1 cm in each direction, per year, so that in 200 million years the Atlantic Ocean has become about 4000 km wide.

The Mid-Atlantic Ridge is high because it is the result of hot mantle convecting upward there. The hot mantle near the surface is expanded, thus its density is smaller than the surrounding cooler mantle. The expanded volume results in a ridge which contributes to shallowing the average depth of the oceans. As the spreading plates part from each other, the original warm mantle near Earth's surface cools and contracts. The contraction results in a progressive deepening of the ocean away from the ridge (Fig. 6–3). The shallowed average ocean basin depth at the start of the spreading of the continents has gradually been deepening. About 200 million years ago the sea lapped up on the continents as deep ocean was replaced by shallow ocean as the Atlantic Ocean began to form. As spreading continued the cooling rock of the thickening lithosphere has gradually increased the mean depth of the

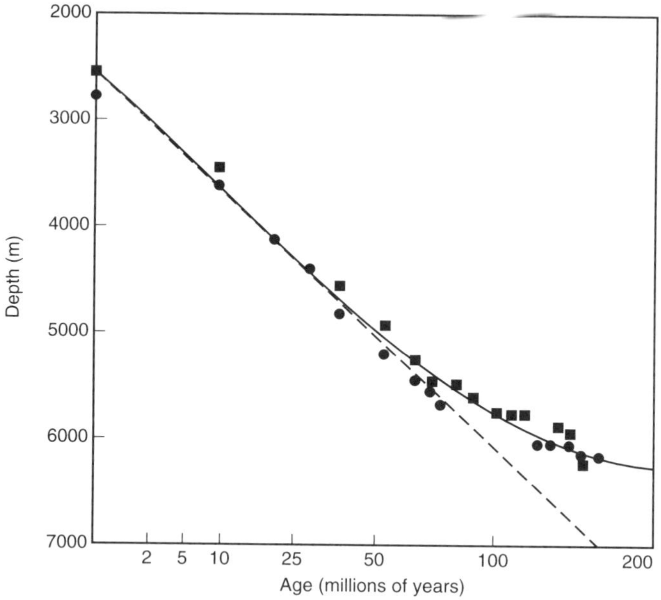

FIGURE 6–3 Plot of the depth of the ocean floor as a function of its age for the North Atlantic (solid squares) and the North Pacific (solid dots). The straight-line plot of the depth vs. the square root of the age for ages less than 60 million years shows that the cooling of the lithosphere by radiation accompanied by shrinkage is operative. (After J. Sclater and C. Tapscott, 1979, *Sci. Am.*, v. 240, no. 6, p. 156. Copyright by Scientific American, Inc. All rights reserved.)

oceans, and the sea generally has been retreating from the continents ever since. The drop in sea level, because of this factor, was several hundred meters over the past 80 million years (the period for which reliable estimates can be made).

The combination of all the effects acting on sea level over the past 80 million years resulted in a gradual decrease in sea level over that period. Global sea level is lower by several hundred meters now than it was 80 million years ago. Yet over the past 2.5 million years, large fluctuations in sea level have occurred as the result of the continental ice storage and melting cycle discussed in Chapter 4. The most recent melting of continental ice sheets continues to have profound effects on coastal processes.

THE LAST 18,000 YEARS OF SEA-LEVEL CHANGE

The peak of the last major continental glaciation occurred 18,000 years ago. Since then the ice sheets on Europe and North America have disappeared.

Although the storage and release back to the oceans of this much frozen water on the continents was known to have a considerable effect on sea level, the amount and the tempo of change was certified from a curious quarter—a semitropical island in the Caribbean.

Barbados is one of the southernmost islands of the Antilles. It is marked by terraces that were formed by the deposition of coral at sea level at the same time that uplift of the island from the sea was occurring in response to the convergence of the Caribbean and Atlantic plates. These terraces, when accurately dated by radioactive means, provide a way of determining the beat of the advance and retreat of the sea at least for the past 130,000 years, as we shall see later. It is not from these well-studied terraces that our insight into the sea-level changes of the last 18,000 years comes, however, but from the study of cores obtained by a drilling ship in the relatively shallow waters around Barbados.

The staghorn coral, *Acropora palmata* (Fig. 6–4), is restricted in a coral reef to a zone within 2 m of the sea surface. Because of this restricted habitat, its presence is a marker of sea level. (Other coral species are characteristic of

FIGURE 6–4 The staghorn coral, *Acropora palmata* (Discovery Bay, Jamaica), grows with its top less than two meters below the ocean surface and is therefore a good index of sea level. (Photographer: W. Sacco.)

greater depths.) As sea level rose since the melting of the continental ice sheets, starting 18,000 years ago, the coral reef kept growing upward, but always with *Acropora* close to the sea level of the time.

With a series of cores obtained by drilling from a ship off the southwest part of Barbados the rise in sea level was documented. Using radioactive methods of dating, the rates of rise of sea level over the past 18,000 years were determined (Fig. 6–5). The sea started rising about 18,000 years ago as the ice began to melt and accelerated from 11,000 to 10,500 years ago, slowed down as a second short ice advance occurred (called the "younger Dryas"), accelerated once again, and then gradually slowed to the virtual constancy of sea level of the past thousand years or so. All in all, within a period of less than 15,000 years, sea level rose 120 meters (400 feet) with sharp increases on a time scale of 2000 years about 11,000 years ago.

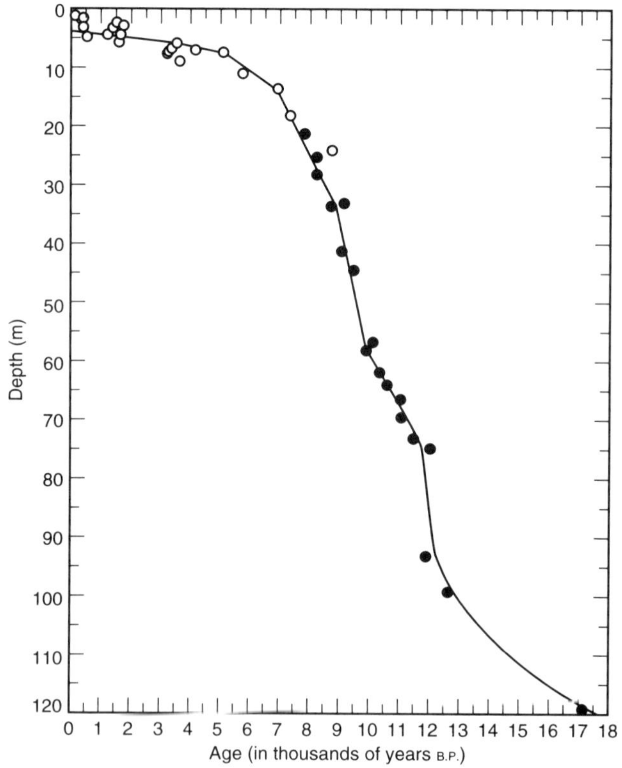

FIGURE 6–5 Barbados sea-level curve based on radiocarbon-dated *Acropora palmata*. Open circles represent data from other Caribbean islands. (After R. Fairbanks, 1989, *Nature,* v. 342, p. 637. Reprinted with permission, copyright Macmillan Magazines Limited.)

SEA-LEVEL CHANGES OVER THE PAST 130,000 YEARS (A GLACIAL AGE CYCLE)

We return now to the raised coral terraces of Barbados and other islands like Haiti and, in the Pacific, New Guinea, similarly rising out of the sea because of the convergence of plates. Because the rates of the spreading of the sea floor have remained reasonably constant, at least over the past 5 million years (see Chapter 1), it is evident that at converging plate boundaries the rate of rise of the upward-rising edge should be moving at a constant rate. When sea level rises at tropical sites reefs build up. When sea level falls, the reefs are left high and dry. Before the next rise in sea level the land will have risen because of the tectonic pressures. The result of this rise and fall of the oceans imprinted on a continuously uplifting island is to yield a series of terraces. The ages of the terraces are the times when sea level was rising. There would be no terraces of any size when sea level retreated again.

With the use of the *Acropora* datum and dating by radioactive methods, a reconstruction of sea-level history over the last glacial cycle can be made when combined with ice storage data inferred from deep-sea cores as described in Chapter 4 (Fig. 6–6). About 125,000 years ago, right after the penultimate major glacial pulse, sea level was about 5 m higher than it is today, indicating the melting of some of the ice in Greenland or Antarctica in addition to the melting of the North American and European ice sheets at that time.

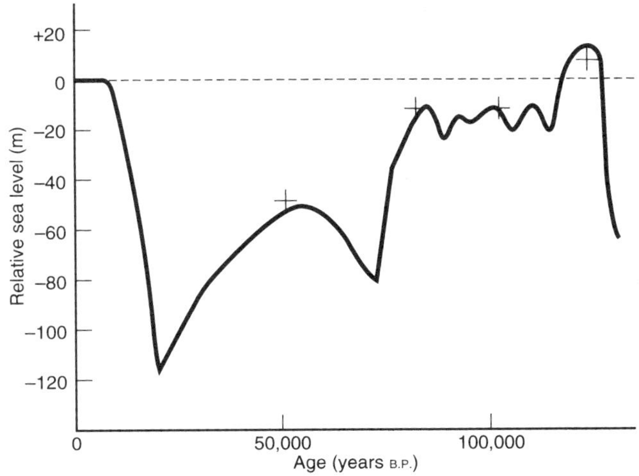

FIGURE 6–6 Inferred sea-level curve from raised coral terraces on Barbados and elsewhere (marked with crosses) and from deep-sea core $\delta^{18}O$ data.

There is a clear relationship between the $\delta^{18}O_c$ of foraminifera in dated core sections and the times of rise and fall of sea level inferred from the island coral terrace data (Fig. 6–6). Since times of high sea level require significant melting of the continental ice sheets, the $\delta^{18}O_c$ would be lowered, and when ice sheets grew, the $\delta^{18}O_c$ would become heavier. If we extract the ice storage effect of the $\delta^{18}O_c$ curves, it provides a measure of sea level as shown in Figure 6–6.

SEA-LEVEL CHANGE AND COASTAL EFFECTS

We now understand that there have been large swings in sea level as the result of ice accumulation on the continents and its melting. The events of the past 18,000 years indicate that the rise in sea level caused by the melting of the continental ice sheets occurred most rapidly over a 2000-year time period about 11,000 years ago. How have the coastlines of Earth responded to these changes in sea level? What will be the effect of further rises in sea level?

When sea level was 120 meters (400 feet) below the present level the configuration of the coastlines was radically different from the present configuration. The gradients of streams draining into the ocean were steeper at their mouths than they are now. The streams carried sediments both from the hinterlands and from the deltas of the previous high sea stand to the ocean. The absence of extensive continental shelves at that time caused these deposits to be dumped into the deep ocean basins. Deep valleys were cut by rivers which, when inundated again, would become Chesapeake Bay, the Persian Gulf, and a host of other bays around the world. Where reef and calcium carbonate bank deposits such as the Bahamas exist now there would have been steep scarps that would hardly be a beckoning site for ice age vacationers!

As sea level rose, sometimes with great speed, and flooded the incised continental shelf, at first small bays were made. Eventually with the decrease in the gradient of the streams, and with higher sea level, the bays, which served as excellent harbors, began to silt up. Troy is an example of an ancient maritime town made powerful by its access both to the sea and the interior through its river and roads. Its demise gave rise to the story of the Iliad with its beachhead-type invasion and siege. Now Troy is deep inland as its once shallow harbor has silted up (Fig. 6–7). If the Greeks did not "the labors of the gods destroy and strike to dust the imperial towers of Troy" (Alexander Pope), the city was certainly doomed as a maritime force by the inevitable silting of its harbor. A similar fate befell the ancient cities of Ephesus, Ostia in Italy, and Ur on the Persian Gulf—all sea coast towns once and now inland cities because of river silting of a previously commanding harbor.

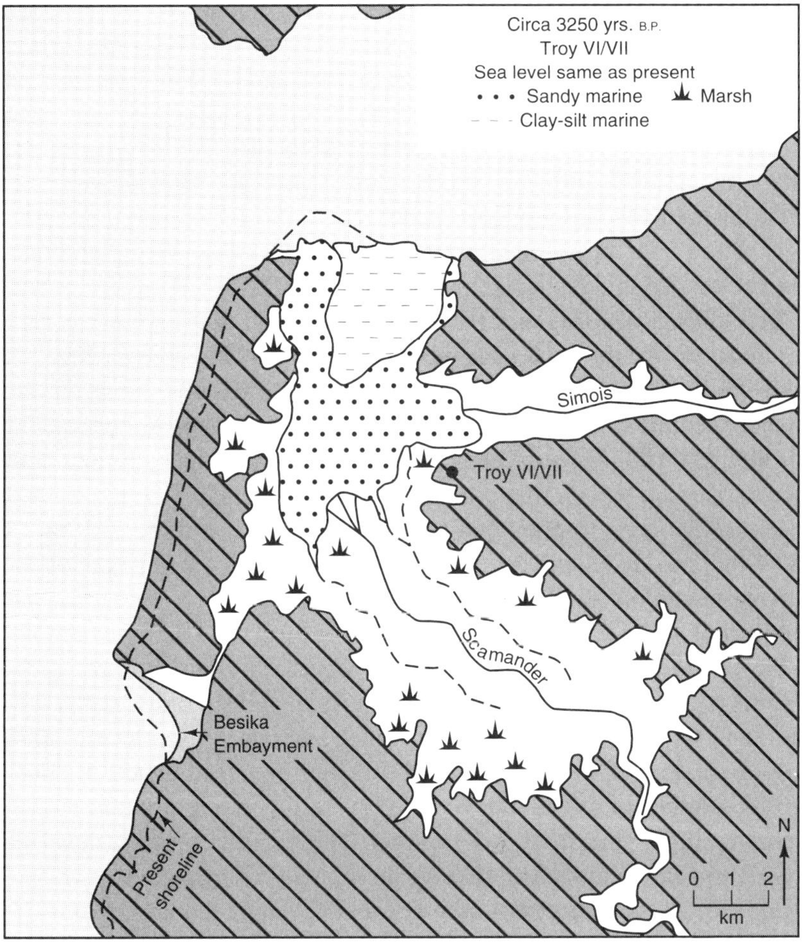

FIGURE 6–7 Radiocarbon-dated sediment cores from the plains around the ancient city of Troy show that it was a marine embayment at the time of the Iliad (3250 B.P.). (Courtesy of J. C. Kraft, University of Delaware.)

Rising sea level also began to erode the relict sediments deposited as the result of continental glaciation on the continental shelves once above sea level. For example, Long Island is composed of terminal moraines resulting from the ice sheets that covered New England and New York State over 11,000 years ago. Between these terminal moraines and what is now Connecticut, a great lake was formed by the melting of the ice sheet. As the ice sheets melted and sea level rose, Long Island and other parts of the terminal moraines, such as Block Island, Martha's Vineyard, and Nantucket, were surrounded by the waters of the Atlantic Ocean. The sea level rose to that height about 7000 years ago. Long Island Sound was then transformed from a postglacial lake into the present-day salty body of water subject to tides and wave action. The intense storm-induced waves along the open Atlantic shore result in the aggressive erosion of the shoreline. The year-by-year erosion of eastern Long Island has threatened classic landmarks such as the Montauk lighthouse. Martha's Vineyard, Nantucket, and Cape Cod, also remnants of terminal moraines of the last glaciation now surrounded by the stormy seas of New England, are also fated to be eroded and reshaped into sandbars.

In addition to silting and erosion, the power of the sea worked on loose sediment stored on the shelves and built the barrier islands from New York to Texas in the United States (Fig. 6–8). The barrier islands, however, are not permanent features, as their response to the seas driven by hurricane-force winds attest. As the result of each storm a fraction of the sediment composing the barrier island is transported via submarine canyons to the deep ocean but a large fraction is trapped by the vast salt marshes and shallow bays landward of the barrier island. By this latter process the barrier islands are the first stage of adding land to the coastline. The future of the barrier islands depends on the rate of supply of new sediment from the streams debouching onto the continental shelf. Barrier islands exist as the direct consequence of the retreat and return of the sea along the continental shelf due to the advance and retreat of continental glaciers. It is the sharp rise in sea level inundating the continental shelf starting 11,000 years ago that established the presence of barrier islands, and it is the interplay of sediment supply and storminess that continually shapes and moves them. The small rise in sea level during the past 100 years plays virtually no role in this grand contest.

Indeed, all the features of silting, erosion, and reshaping by transport of the coastline are direct consequences of the major oscillations of sea level over 400 feet (120 m) on time scales of tens of thousands of years and are not related to the recent rise of about a foot (around 20 cm) in the last 100 years.

WHAT ABOUT THE FUTURE OF SEA-LEVEL RISE?

The one foot rise in sea level over the past 100 years accompanied the general increase in atmospheric temperature and the increase in CO_2 (and methane) in the atmosphere. Some believe that these three trends are related, although the other factor in temperature variation, the radiance of the sun, may be implicated as part of the cause of the rise in temperature.

The retreat of valley glaciers (Fig. 6–9) is compatible with both the observed global warming and small rise in sea level. The warming causes

(a)

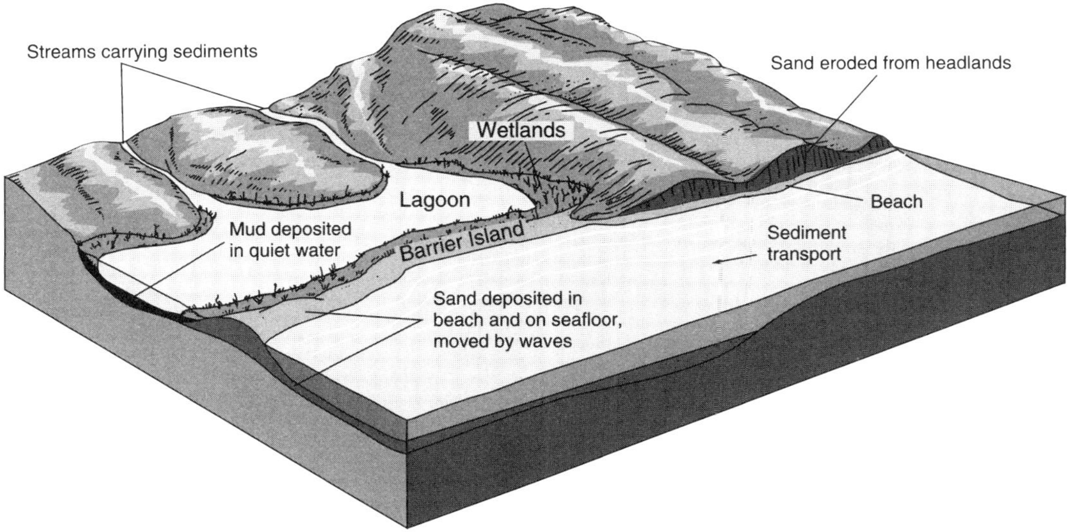

(b)

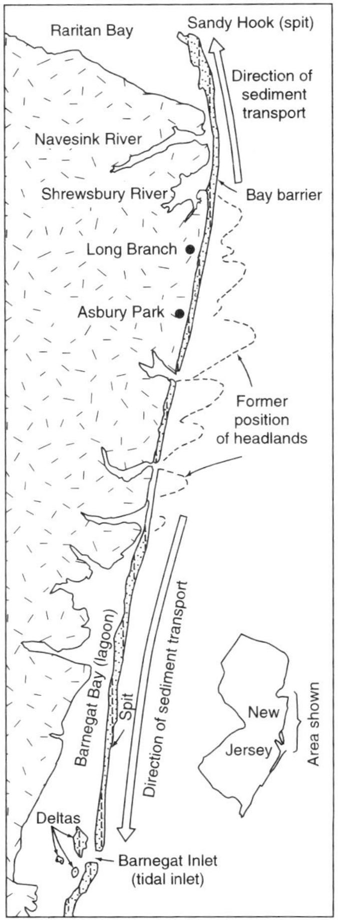

FIGURE 6–8 Barrier islands (or beaches): (a) cross section of the coastal zone; (b) a map of the New Jersey shore showing the forces acting to shape the coastline as the result of sea level-rise and resulting action of the oceans. (After G. Gross, 1993, *Oceanography*, Prentice Hall.)

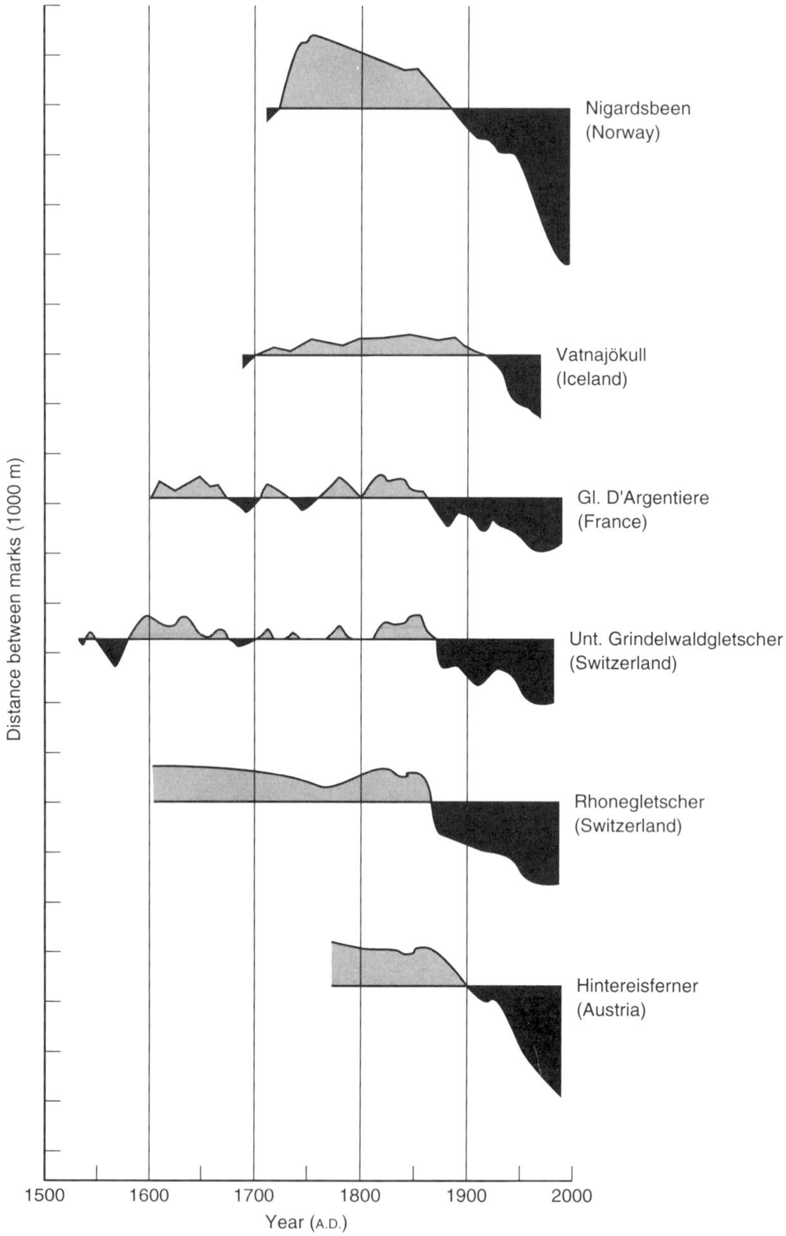

FIGURE 6–9 Valley glaciers throughout Europe (and Iceland) have been retreating since the latter part of the eighteenth century. (From *Climate Change,* 1990, Report of IPCC Working Group 1, Cambridge University Press.)

valley glaciers to retreat because the rate of ablation exceeds the rate of snow delivery. The decrease in the amount of valley glacial ice shows up as an increase in the amount of water in the oceans.

Another consequence of atmospheric warming is that the oceans also warm up. As sea water warms it expands, resulting in an increased volume which causes a rise in sea-level. Satellite measurements relating global sea-surface temperature and sea-level rise show this effect over the past several years (Fig. 6–10).

A third way in which human activity has caused a rise in sea level does not relate to the observed increase in global temperature but to the fact that water stored in groundwater reservoirs and lakes is utilized in irrigation in many places in this world and in the process, water is subject to evaporation and ultimately delivered to the oceans. A recent estimate of this effect (Table 6–1) suggests that a part of the sea level rise over the past 100 years may be due to this effect.

The natural expectation is to conclude that if indeed temperature increases further, sea level will also. This assumption is based on the expectation

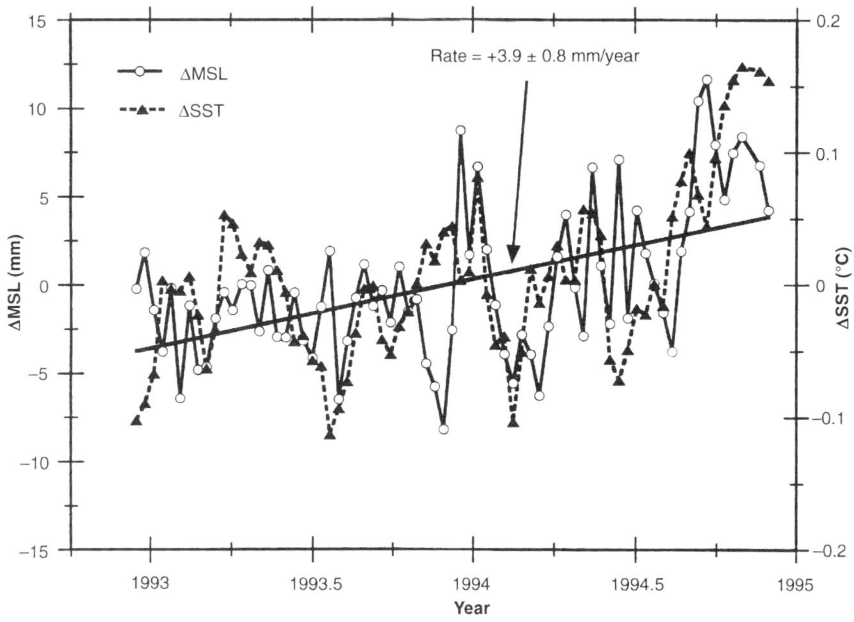

FIGURE 6–10 Global sea-level rise (ΔMSL = change in mean sea level) between 1993 and 1995 as measured by the TOPEX/POSEIDON satellite compared with global sea surface temperature rise (ΔSST = change in sea surface temperature) for the same period. (Reprinted with permission from R. S. Nerem, 1995, *Science,* v. 268, p. 708. Copyright American Association for the Advancement of Science.)

TABLE 6–1 Anthropogenic contributions to sea level rise over the past 100 years

Water reservoir	Present net extraction rate ($\times 10^{10}$ m^3 yr^{-1})	Sea-level rise rate (mm yr^{-1})	Estimated sea-level change to date (mm)
United States			
High plains	1.2	0.03	1.1
Southwest	1.0	0.03	0.92
California	1.3	0.04	1.2
Africa and Asia			
Sahara	1.0	0.03	0.56
Arabia	1.6	0.04	0.89
Aral (lake)			
1960	2.7	0.08	2.2
Aral (groundwater)	3.7	0.1	3.1
Caspian (lake)	0.77	0.02	1.3
Caspian (groundwater)	0.47	0.01	0.78
Sahel (soil water)	0.34	0.01	0.28
Worldwide			
Deforestation	4.9	0.14	3.4
Wetland reduction	0.2	0.006	1.3
Dams	–	–	–5.2
Total	19.2	0.54	11.8

After D. L. Sahagian, F. W. Schwartz, and D. K. Jacobs, 1994, *Nature,* v. 367, p. 54.

that as the result of the increase in temperature there will be a gradual decrease in the ice stored in Greenland and Antarctica. Is such an assumption valid? A legitimate counterargument to this assumption is that with an increase in temperature, sea level can be lowered as ice caps actually grow in size. As the temperature of the lower troposphere increases, the average ocean surface temperature increases and the water vapor content of the atmosphere increases. As this water-enriched air is transported toward the polar land masses such as Antarctica and Greenland, which are maintained at subfreezing temperatures, more snow accumulates on the ice cap than at cooler and drier times. The record from ice cores from Antarctica (Fig. 6–11) seems to confirm this expectation as the rate of snow accumulation during the peak of glaciation is considerably lower than the present rate or that of the prior "interglacial" time period (between 70,000 years and 125,000 years ago).

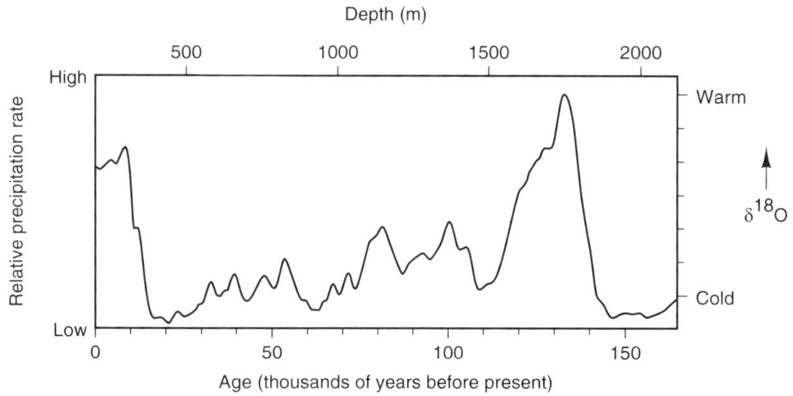

FIGURE 6–11 The rate of precipitation, based on the assumption of a constant flux of cosmic ray-produced ^{10}Be (half-life = 1.5 million years), on Antarctica is inversely related to air temperature as reflected in the $\delta^{18}O$ of the accumulated snow. (After C. Lorius, G. Raisbeck, J. Jouzel, and D. Raynaud, 1989, p. 341–361 in *The Environmental Record in Glaciers and Ice Sheets*, eds. H. Oeschger and C. C. Langway, Jr., Wiley-Interscience Publications.)

There are also observations in Greenland, based on satellite data over the past ten years, that indicate that ice has actually been accumulating there even as the worldwide atmospheric temperature has been increasing. Also most of the Antarctic ice cap is either growing or remaining the same (Fig. 6–12) based on field studies. Thus the ice caps may be increasing in the amount of water stored rather than decreasing during the recent warming period. If this indeed is the case, the worldwide rise in sea level of 20 cm over the past 100 years could all be ascribed to the decline in valley glaciers, the warming of the oceans, and possibly to human-accelerated pumping of old, stored groundwater for irrigation, and therefore cannot be extrapolated into the future except as these three processes are involved. The major ice sheets appear to be growing or holding their own and are therefore not a cause of the observed sea level rise.

What would happen if sea level rose an additional 5 m at a rate of 0.20 cm per year, much as it did over the past 100 years? The shoreline would adjust to this rise so that silting, erosion, and transport would shape, in a slow and almost imperceptible fashion, the features of the present coastlines much as it is happening now. Effectively, humans respond to such a rate of change easily because it is slow enough to result in rebuilding or relocating. Certain coastal areas, such as Bangladesh at the mouth of the Ganges and Brahmaputra Rivers, would also be affected, but the dominant problem in Bangladesh is a massive

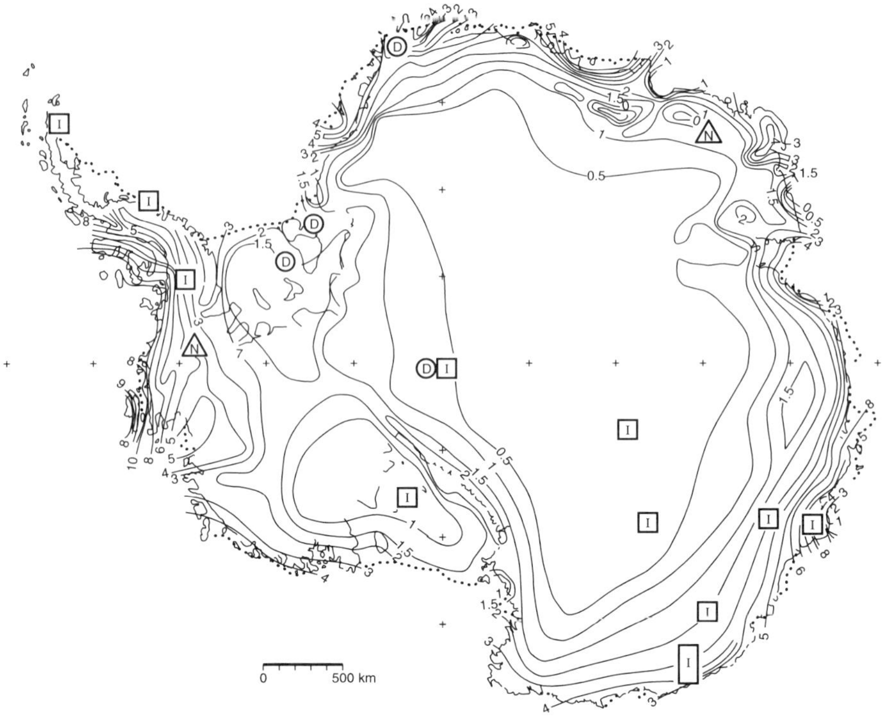

FIGURE 6–12 Estimates of the behavior of the Antarctic ice cap over the past approximately 30 years. The present day accumulation rates are contoured in units of 100 kg $m^{-2}y^{-1}$. I = increase, D = decrease, N = neutral, over the time period measured. (Compilation by S. S. Jacobs, 1992, *Nature,* v. 360, p. 29. Reprinted with permission, copyright Macmillan Magazines Limited.)

reproduction rate, human hostilities in the surrounding region, and the building of dams and levees along the rivers further upstream. Sea-level rise is the least of the troubles of Bangladesh.

If, however, sea level rose very sharply as the result of a virtually instantaneous melting of a part of the Antarctic ice sheet, then the consequences would be more severe. The part of the sheet most vulnerable to this process is expected to be what is called the West Antarctic ice sheet. Detailed studies of this sector of the Antarctic ice sheet indicate that the ice sheet has either been growing or remaining constant over the past tens of years. This observation was made using layers of volcanic ash or artificial tinsel-like material to determine the accumulation rate while directly measuring the loss by ablation. Indeed, based on the mass of ice involved, the ice sheet's movement is responsive to the environmental memory of a thousand years ago rather than the recent past or the foreseeable future.

PROBLEM:

A. There is a relationship between depth to bottom (corrected for any sediment thickness present) and age in all the oceans. This relationship is

$$d = 2500 + 345\ t^{1/2}$$

where

$$d = \text{depth in meters}$$
$$t = \text{age in millions of years}$$

1. For one side of a spreading center along a traverse perpendicular to the axis of the spreading center, show the increase in area of ocean water, plotting depth against distance from the ridge crest (0 age: 2500 meters depth) after 36 million years for each of the velocities of spreading given below:
   (a) 1 cm per year (typical of the Atlantic Ocean)
   (b) 10 cm per year (typical of the Pacific Ocean)
2. What is the approximate depth of water in the Pacific where convergence occurs and oceanic crust is subducted?
3. If a rift in a continent developed into a true spreading center, what would happen to sea level around the world?

B. Sea-level change by ice storage and melting.

1. If the Antarctic and Greenland ice caps should all melt, what would be the worldwide rise in sea level? Assume the following:
   - The area of the oceans = 362×10^6 km^2
   - The mean depth of the oceans = 3730 meters
   - The volume of ice in the Antarctic and Greenland caps = 29×10^6 km^3.
2. If the average salinity of the oceans before melting was 35.5 parts per thousand (grams of total dissolved salts per 1000 grams of seawater), what would it be after the great melt-down of question 1 occurred?
3. If the actual mean $\delta^{18}O$ value of the oceans was –0.16 prior to melting of the ice caps and the mean $\delta^{18}O$ value of the ice caps is –40.00, what will the mean $\delta^{18}O$ of the oceans be after the great melt-down?
4. Earth is a sphere—actually a slightly oblate spheroid because of its rotation "flattening" at the poles and "swelling" at the equator. The mass of a wedge of the planet from the surface to the core at any particular latitude tends to remain constant *(isostasy).* If a mass is removed from the surface at a location, as by the melting of an ice cap, material is supplied by flow in the mantle to restore the mass that was lost, causing the land to rise. This rate of isostatic uplift depends on a number of factors, but mainly on the viscosity of the mantle. (For this reason land on which there was once an ice cap, such as

Scandinavia, appears to be rising from the sea.) If the thickness of the ice melted in question 1 was 2 km and the density of compressed ice and mantle material are 1 g cm^{-3} and 3.3 g cm^{-3}, respectively, how much would the Antarctic continent rise relative to the new sea level when isostatic equilibrium is reached after the melting? (Remember to include the effect of the mass of the added water to the ocean basins.)

7

CARBON DIOXIDE, METHANE, AND GLOBAL WARMING

The powerful and intricate forces of nature far transcend the puny efforts of humans to disturb the universe. Yet the immediate environment in which humans, and indeed all of life as we know it, exist is a thin veneer on a small planet. From this platform we dare to try to understand the universe. We also have the capacity to influence the properties of our observatory both locally and globally. It is true that the variations of the solar output of energy, the orbital constants of the planets, and Earth's own response to energy loss from the interior can never be influenced by any of our efforts, no matter how heroic or foolish. Our efforts, however, in altering the composition of the atmosphere and the surface of the planet can already be seen by good, ground-based observations and from satellites. The most dramatic change in our atmosphere has been the increase in carbon dioxide.

Since 1957, accurate measurements of the carbon dioxide concentration of air have been made systematically beginning at Mauna Loa on the "big island" of Hawaii (see Fig. 3–1 on page 45) and subsequently extended to a number of locations ranging from Antarctica to the equator. All of these sites show that the concentration of carbon dioxide in the atmosphere is increasing. This increase amounts to a change of carbon dioxide concentration from 280 parts per million per volume of air (ppmv) in 1957 to about 356 ppmv in 1992. By measuring gases in ice cores, we know that the level of atmospheric CO_2 started to increase in about 1860. If current trends continue, perhaps by the year 2100 the carbon dioxide will be twice what it was before the modern industrial age began in earnest around 1860. An increase in the amount of carbon dioxide in the atmosphere may result in warming and is the basis for the current concern about environmental and societal impacts of "global warming."

Carbon dioxide is one of the "greenhouse" gases. Water vapor, by far, is the most important greenhouse gas, but carbon dioxide makes a significant contribution to the effect. The question we must ask is what incremental effect the increasing CO_2 concentration will have on the annual temperature and climate in general. If there is a significant effect above the normal variability of climate, can humans adapt to these effects without major dislocations and possible turmoil? Humanity survived the 5°C lowering of worldwide temperature during the ice ages and 1.5°C lowering during the "Little Ice Age" culminating in the latter part of the seventeenth century. Indeed, global warming at both times would have been perceived as a good thing. With a present-day population of 5 billion people and counting, however, would a further increase in temperature, no matter how small, be too much of a good thing? Would it influence climate in such a way that society would be grossly affected in a negative way? These are the questions that drive the debate about global warming.

THE CONTROLS ON THE CARBON DIOXIDE CONCENTRATION IN THE AIR

The carbon at the surface of Earth is partitioned among several reservoirs. These are shown in Table 7–1. The largest reservoir by far is in sedimentary rocks. The carbonate minerals of biogenic origin found in limestones hold about twice as much carbon as found in organic matter in sedimentary rocks including coal and oil. These reservoirs hold a hundred times more carbon than the next largest reservoir, the oceans. Living matter on land and sea is about fifty times less than the dissolved inorganic carbon (dissolved CO_2, bicarbonate ion and carbonate ion) in the oceans.

If the ocean, with calcium carbonate deposits along its boundary as sediments, and the atmosphere were totally in equilibrium with each other, the CO_2 pressure in the atmosphere would be determined by the temperature of the oceans and the acidity (pH) of the oceans (Appendix 7–1): The warmer the oceans, the more CO_2 in the atmosphere; the greater the acidity of the oceans, the higher the CO_2 in the atmosphere. The equilibrium between the ocean and atmosphere is maintained through the top layer of the ocean that is intimately in contact with the atmosphere. The surface layer of the ocean (say the top 100 meters) is being generated by upwelling of the water from greater depths and the surface water eventually is returned to depth. The top 100 meters stays in intimate contact with the atmosphere for tens of years

TABLE 7–1 The Carbon Reservoirs at Earth's Surface

	10^{10} moles C
Sediments	
Carbonate	91,000
Organic carbon	50,000
Ocean	
Dissolved inorganic	320
Upper 100 meters	6
Living matter and organic debris	
Marine	14.1
Continental	2.3
Atmosphere	5.3

before submergence, and the deep water remains in the 4000-meters-deep reservoir for a thousand years or so before coming once again into contact with the atmosphere. On the time scale of a thousand years, the atmosphere and the ocean therefore tend to be in equilibrium and will regulate the amount of carbon dioxide in the atmosphere.

When we consider shorter time scales we must look specifically at what happens in the three most directly interacting reservoirs, the surface ocean, the atmosphere, and living matter both terrestrial and marine. These three reservoirs each have about the same amount of carbon so that any change in one of these interactive reservoirs will affect the others. The surface ocean responds to the atmospheric increase in CO_2 by dissolving more of it. This dissolved carbon dioxide is partially transformed into living matter which, through the cycle of life and particle settling, transmits the increased atmospheric CO_2 signal to depth. The submergence of surface water, which has begun to equilibrate with the atmosphere, also transports the CO_2 signal throughout the oceans.

Roughly half of the CO_2 released by fossil fuel burning is found in the atmosphere, the other half being removed elsewhere. Until recently it was thought that the surface oceans were the sink (via the pathways described), but measurements made at sea on the actual exchange time of CO_2 between ocean and atmosphere suggest that half of the "missing" CO_2 may be found in the terrestrial storage of carbon. There is evidence that since the massive clearing (over a century ago) of forests for conversion to farmland, there has been an increase in woodlands. This "global greening," as some have called it, is mainly the consequence of new growth because of changes in land use, but some of it may be due to increased general growth ascribable to the increase in the availability of CO_2 for photosynthesis.

THE RECORD OF ATMOSPHERIC CARBON DIOXIDE CONCENTRATION CHANGES DURING THE LAST 150,000 YEARS

The great ice caps in Antarctica, and to a lesser extent Greenland, provide a record of continuous ice accumulation over at least 150,000 years. We therefore have a record of at least one major glacial cycle. As snow gradually accumulates in these areas and is buried, it passes from its original, low density, porous state to solid ice. The atmospheric gases included in the porous snow are trapped in the solid ice either as small bubbles or as part of the crystal structure of the ice.

As ice accumulates, the deeper parts flow away toward the edge of the ice sheet under the burden of accumulating ice. This flow thins the annual layers more and more with increasing depth in the ice sheet. By modeling this flow behavior, the age of each layer in an ice core can be determined and the composition of the trapped atmospheric gas for that time can be measured.

From the trapped atmospheric gases a record of the carbon dioxide concentration of the atmosphere can be inferred by creating a ratio to the dominant gas in the atmosphere, nitrogen, which is presumed to remain constant over time. Other atmospheric gas concentrations are also determinable by this method. For example, we now know that the changes in concentrations of methane and oxygen as well as aerosols, such as products of volcanism and ocean productivity, occurred during the great climatic cycles of the last hundreds of thousands of years.

The changes in the oxygen isotope ratio in the ice itself provide insights into the way global temperature has changed when compared to the paleontologic and oxygen isotope record in deep-sea cores. The results obtained from an ice core from Antarctica are shown in Figure 7–1. The strong correlation of the CO_2 content of the atmosphere with global temperature is evident: the lower the global temperature, the lower the CO_2 concentration of the atmosphere. Clearly there is a relationship between CO_2 and climate on the time scale of the ice ages, but are the changes in CO_2 determining global temperatures or the other way around?

The most likely view is that carbon dioxide concentration in the atmosphere is driven by climate rather than the other way around. A strong argument comes from the fact that methane, another greenhouse gas that we will discuss later, also generally varies with CO_2 and therefore climate. The concentrations of these two gases then appear to be driven by the same force—namely the change in climate.

How is the CO_2 concentration in the air determined by climate? Although the answer is complex and not thoroughly understood, we do have some intimations from the study of the behavior of the oceans under different

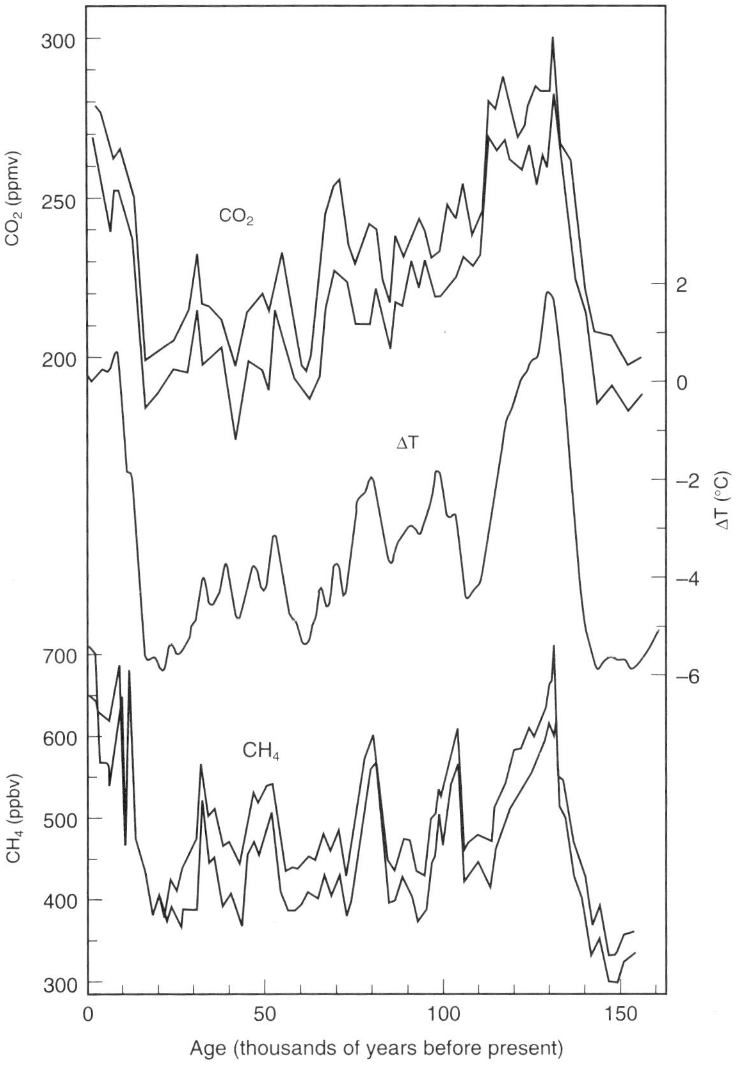

FIGURE 7–1 The variation of CO_2 and methane over time as inferred from an ice core (Vostok) from Antarctica (from J. M. Barnola, D. Raynaud, Y. S. Korotkevich, and C. Lorius, 1987, *Nature,* v. 329, p. 408, and J. Chappellaz, J. M. Barnola, D. Raynaud, and Y. S. Korotkevich, 1990, *Nature,* v. 345, p. 127.) The envelope for each curve represents the range of values observed for each period of time. The temperature is based on oxygen isotope studies of the ice (from C. Lorius, J. Jouzel, D. Raynaud, J. Hansen, and H. Le Treut, 1990, *Nature,* v. 347, p. 139.) (From *Climate Change*, 1990, Report of IPCC Working Group 1, Cambridge University Press.)

climatic conditions. The most obvious effect is that gases dissolve more in cold than in warm water. The surface layer of the ocean then would tend to dissolve more CO_2 and the atmospheric concentration would go down as the temperature dropped.

We turn now to scenarios that couple the CO_2 in the atmosphere and biological productivity in the surface oceans. If there were greater rates of photosynthesis during glacial times relative to the present time, possibly because of increased rate of upwelling, then there would be a tendency for CO_2 to be "pumped" from the atmosphere into the ocean at a greater rate. If the return of CO_2 from the oxidation of organic matter at depth in the oceans was not rapid and complete, then CO_2 in the atmosphere might be maintained at a low level. If, however, the rate of return of carbon dioxide produced by respiration in the ocean depths was rapid, then there would not necessarily be a decrease in the atmospheric level of CO_2.

A variant of the biologically controlled mechanism for atmospheric CO_2 control during glacial cycles depends on the different types of organisms responsible for the carbon cycle in the surface oceans. We know that phosphorus and nitrogen compounds are necessary for the sustenance of life (assuming that carbon and water are not limiting). All organisms have these elements in soft tissue roughly in the proportion of 1 atom of P to 15 atoms of N to 130 atoms of C (the "Redfield ratio," named after its formulator, Alfred Redfield). Many organisms have hard parts, including phosphatic chitonic carapaces (as in lobsters and shrimp) and internal skeletons (as in fish and marine mammals), calcium carbonate ($CaCO_3$), silica (SiO_2), and even strontium sulfate.

If we concentrate on the most common forms having hard parts, we identify the photosynthesizing calcium carbonate-depositing coccolithophoridae and the silica-depositing diatoms. Both of these organisms are unicellular and are responsible for establishing the food chain in the oceans (Figure 7–2). They are called autotrophes. Down the food chain are other single-celled organisms, including the calcium carbonate-depositing foraminifera and silica-depositing radiolaria (Figure 7–2). These belong to the category of organisms called heterotrophes. Deep-sea deposits contain all four of these hard part remains but not in equal proportions. The amount of each type of test reaching the ocean bottom depends on the efficiency of production of each and the survival of the test in its transit through the water column.

How can we use this information to help us understand the fluctuation of CO_2 in the atmosphere during the glacial cycle? The answer lies in the difference in the way carbon is transferred from the ocean surface to depth by organisms depositing calcium carbonate tests and those depositing silica

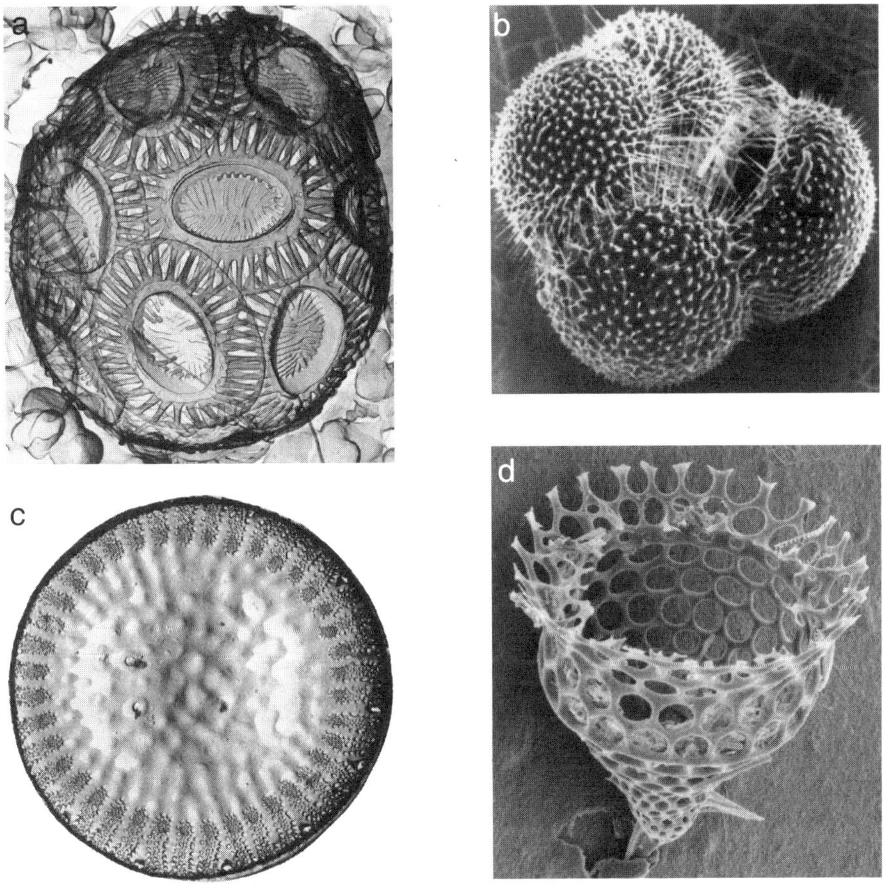

FIGURE 7–2 Planktonic organisms. Coccoliths (a) and foraminifera (b) deposit calcium carbonate tests. Diatoms (c) and radiolaria (d) deposit silica tests. The sizes range from 0.5 millimeters down. (Photos courtesy of A. McIntyre, E. Thomas, P. E. Hargraves and C. McClintock.)

tests. When calcium carbonate is deposited from seawater, effectively the following reaction takes place:

$$Ca^{++} + 2(HCO_3^-) = CaCO_3 + H_2O + CO_2$$

so that for every molecule of calcium carbonate deposited, one molecule of CO_2 is released. When silica is deposited, however, no CO_2 is released. If we presume that the organic fraction of both siliceous (silica-depositing) and calcareous (calcium carbonate-depositing) organisms are derived from the same CO_2 pool, then obviously if silica-depositing organisms predominate, CO_2 will be extracted from the atmosphere and act as a "biological pump," whereas if calcium carbonate-depositing organisms predominate, then CO_2 will be added to the surface water and ultimately released to the atmosphere.

Ocean chemistry, temperature, and global climate seem to affect the ratio of silica-depositing organisms to calcium carbonate-depositing organisms. The coldest surface waters in the oceans are around the Arctic and Antarctic regions. In these regions the dominant organisms observed in the water and preserved in deep-sea deposits are siliceous diatoms and radiolaria. If there is a correlation between the coldness of surface waters and the ratio of siliceous to calcareous organisms, then during cold times the "biological pumping" of CO_2 from the atmosphere would be more important (because of the dominance of non-CO_2-releasing silica test deposition) than CO_2 release (from the less dominant CO_2-releasing calcium carbonate deposition). Clearly a temperature effect is operating. There is also a chemical effect based on the concentration of dissolved silica in the oceans. The deep-sea sediments in the Pacific are richer in siliceous organisms relative to calcareous organisms compared to the Atlantic. We observe that the dissolved silica content of the Pacific Ocean is between two and four times that in the Atlantic. The high concentration of dissolved silica obviously enhances the production of siliceous tests.

The oxidation of organic matter associated with silica tests contributes CO_2 to deep water tending toward a drop in pH whereas when organic matter associated with calcareous tests is oxidized at depth, the reaction with the associated calcium carbonate tends toward the neutralization of the acidity that would have formed by the reverse of the reaction given above. That is

$$CaCO_3 + CO_2 + H_2O = (Ca^{++}) + 2(HCO_3^-)$$

with no production of hydrogen ions. We observe that the pH of deep Pacific water is lower than deep Atlantic water and at least part of this difference is due to the relative importance of silica and calcium carbonate-depositing organisms—higher silica to calcium carbonate in the Pacific relative to the Atlantic.

How do these observations contribute to our understanding of the variation in CO_2 shown in Figure 7–1? For one thing the surface oceans were definitely cooler during the peak of glaciation. If contemporary observations are extended to the past, this would mean more siliceous than calcareous organisms dominating photosynthetic and heterotrophic life. Less CO_2 would be released to the atmosphere. In addition, the concentration of silica in the oceans would be larger during glacial times since lowered sea level would diminish the number of estuarine sites of silica removal, thereby tending to increase the dissolved silica content carried by streams into the oceans. The enhanced silica concentration in the oceans would further enhance the chance of the siliceous-depositing pathway for both primary productivity and secondary deposition.

Undoubtedly the lowering of CO_2 in the atmosphere would contribute to cooling but it would not in itself be the driving force. The climatic cycle driven by other forces, probably modulated by the Milankovitch cycle discussed, is dominant, and the CO_2 in the atmosphere responds to this forcing through the changes in the chemistry and biological make-up of the oceans.

LONGER TIMESCALE CHANGES IN ATMOSPHERIC CARBON DIOXIDE

Theory and measurements indicate that Earth's atmosphere has undergone large swings in the CO_2 concentration. We have seen that the earliest atmosphere was probably enriched in carbon dioxide, perhaps helping to maintain the surface warmth of the planet. Variations of the CO_2 concentration in the atmosphere must have occurred throughout the history of Earth in large part due to the effects of life. We will focus on the variations over the past 100 million years for which we have a strong geologic record of changes in sea level, life, mountain-building rate, and climate.

As indicated, the equilibrium value of the carbon dioxide content of the atmosphere is controlled by the pH (acidity) of the ocean and the temperature. How are these properties determined? We first consider the pH of the ocean. Clearly this property depends on the delivery of acid or base to a solution. If we start with a "titration flask" called the ocean, lined with an acid-soluble lining undergoing slow solution under the proper conditions (we have identified this material as calcium carbonate), we can follow what happens as acid is added to our flask. But first we must identify the source of the acid. On the short time scale, in a renewable fashion the transport of organic matter to depth and its oxidation produces carbonic acid. In the cycle of life, much of this acid is neutralized by freshly deposited calcium carbonate in the oceans so that even if there are small differences in pH due to the slowness of stirring, eventually the reaction does take place and the "excess" calcium carbonate, brought in by continental weathering, accumulates on the bottom of the ocean. The "excess" calcium carbonate comes from the weathering of limestones deposited in previous epochs of Earth history.

A major source of acid in the ocean basins, beyond the biological recycling, is from marine hydrothermal vents along the major spreading ridges produced in the mantle convection cycle leading to plate tectonics (as discussed in Chapter 1). The pH of the 350°C water coming through the vents is about 4 (when measured at 25°C compared to a "neutral" pH of 7). The oceans have a pH slightly more alkaline than neutral (pH of about 7.7). As each hydrogen ion is added it will transform a carbonate ($CO_3^=$) ion to a bicarbonate (HCO_3^-) ion, which in turn releases CO_2 to the atmosphere unless it can be neutralized by the calcium carbonate lining first. The delay in reaction time can increase the supply of CO_2 to the atmosphere.

Another source of calcium carbonate is available for titration of the added acid. This source is the weathering of the land containing ancient calcium carbonate deposits called limestones. The carbon dioxide content of the atmosphere will then respond to the efficiency of these sources of acid neutralization.

Suppose we add acid to our titration flask from the hydrothermal vent burette. Until reaction takes place with the calcium carbonate lining of the flask the pH of the solution will be low, but it will not remain as low as it might be in a solution not buffered by the different dissolved inorganic carbon-bearing species, carbonate ($CO_3^=$), bicarbonate (HCO_3^-), and dissolved CO_2. The conversion of carbonate to bicarbonate, as we saw, releases CO_2 to the atmosphere.

Now, as the system settles down to a steady state of acid supply and neutralization the CO_2 in the atmosphere may vary slightly, responding to secondary control by seasonal and longer term processes determined by the biological forces previously discussed. If, however, we add a new bit of action to the process by increasing the availability of a neutralizing base, the system responds by decreasing the amount of CO_2 in the atmosphere. The increasing rate of weathering of deposits of calcium carbonate and silicate rocks on land is the result of mountain building. As the pH tends to increase, by our elementary equation, this tends to lower the CO_2 level in the atmosphere.

Thus plate tectonics becomes a significant factor in the control of the CO_2 content of the atmosphere. If the rate of supply of hydrogen ions from hydrothermal vents increases, the atmospheric CO_2 will increase if all else remains the same. If mountain building increases the rate of weathering of limestones and other rocks, the atmospheric carbon dioxide will decrease. As the carbon dioxide content of the atmosphere decreases it tends to reinforce the trend toward global cooling.

What evidence do we have of the lowering of CO_2 in the atmosphere and of its relation to the increased weathering and erosion of mountains? Coring of the deep-sea sediments provides a way of obtaining a worldwide inventory of both biogenic deposits formed from calcareous and siliceous tests and detrital deposits. Figure 7–3 shows that the rate of deep-sea accumulation of nonbiogenic sediments increased dramatically about 15 million years ago. This is the time continental glaciation of Antarctica was underway and the Himalayas and

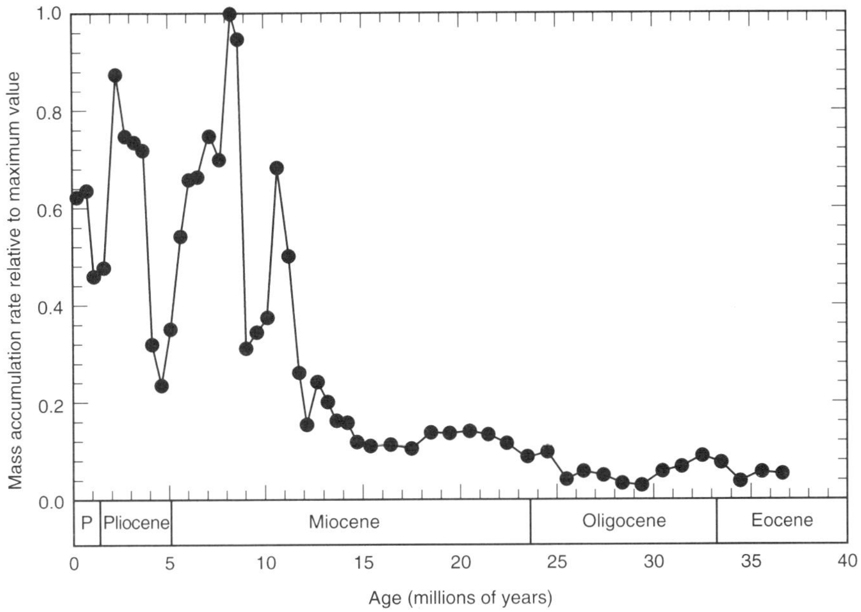

FIGURE 7–3 The increase in sediment accumulation rate in the Indian Ocean reflecting the rise of the Himalayas and the associated Tibetan plateau. The curve represents the mean flux of the nonbiogenic sediment flux as measured in 11 ocean drilling cores. (After D. K. Rea, 1992, *Am. Geophys. Union Monograph* 70, p. 367. Copyright American Geophysical Union.)

Tibetan Plateau were being formed. This increased weathering effectively adds alkalinity to the oceans. If this exceeds the rate of acid supply from hydrothermal vents it will result in a net lowering of the CO_2 content of the atmosphere. A study of the change in the abundances of CO_2-sensitive flora shows that about 7 million years ago there was probably a significant drop in the CO_2 concentration of the atmosphere (see Appendix 7–2).

METHANE

Methane is another of the greenhouse gases. It is also known as marsh gas or natural gas and these designations give us a partial clue to its origin in the atmosphere. The present concentration of methane in the atmosphere is 1.7 ppmv, but in 1860 it was 0.7 ppmv. Therefore, more than a doubling of methane concentration has occurred during the same interval in which about a 25% increase has occurred for carbon dioxide. The importance of methane lies in the fact that as a greenhouse gas it is twenty times more effective than carbon dioxide as an energy absorber and its effect is added to the carbon dioxide effect since the two gases absorb infrared radiation of different wavelengths.

The sources of methane are several and they are of about equal importance. Releases of fossil natural gas occur either by normal seepage or by human projects such as oil and gas wells and coal mining. Wetlands are important sites for the production of methane (hence the name "marsh gas"). In addition to natural wetlands, human-made "wetlands" in the form of rice paddies are at least as important as natural wetlands as a methane source. Ruminants also release vast amounts of methane as a result of their digestive process. Lastly, biomass burning is an important source of methane as well as other gases in the form of nitrogen and sulfur compounds and carbon monoxide. Biomass burning occurs in grasslands, sometimes by natural processes such as lightning but primarily now by human activity such as land clearing, agricultural field processing, and primitive methods of hunting game in tribal Africa. It has been estimated that the most important source of methane on the African continent is biomass burning.

Methane, like carbon dioxide, also changed with the changing climate of the past 130,000 years as determined from ice cores (Fig. 7–1). The increase and decrease of methane during the ice age cycles may be related to the fact that at lower temperature the production of methane is attenuated in soils and wetlands, and also some major wetland sources may have been diminished by both lowered sea level and more ice cover. Actually there is a strong correlation of the methane concentration in the atmosphere during the glacial cycles and the 20,000-year precession cycle involved in orbital forcing, indicating that the sunlight flux during the summer in the northern hemisphere (where the predominance of land is) is the dominant control on methane in the air. The exact mechanism is not known but it must involve the moist tundras of the north as well as the expanding and contracting of wetlands with changes in the intensity of monsoons.

GLOBAL CLIMATE MODELING OF FUTURE CHANGES DUE TO THE ANTHROPOGENIC INCREASE IN ATMOSPHERIC CARBON DIOXIDE

In an attempt to understand how the atmosphere behaves, and to predict the way this behavior will change if one or another of the controlling parameters changes, scientists have been using computers. These computer-generated models based on fundamental physical principles generally are called General Circulation Models or GCMs. From such models a description of the present-day temperature, precipitation, and wind field distributions on Earth are simulated. The area defining each point, however, must be large (hundreds of square miles) for the computer to be able to manage the massive calculation load. GCMs therefore cannot normally describe the differences within, say, the state of Connecticut because of this crudeness of sampling.

One parameter in the models is the concentration of the radiatively important gases such as carbon dioxide and water vapor. Water vapor is strongly controlled by the mean surface temperature of the oceans. Carbon dioxide concentration, however, has been increasing in the atmosphere since about the 1860s. As a greenhouse gas, the increase in carbon dioxide would increase the temperature at Earth's surface on the basis of the elementary principles of radiation. Indeed most GCMs show that if the carbon dioxide content of the atmosphere were doubled, the temperature increase at Earth's surface would be about 3°C (Fig. 7–4).

Two additional important parameters must be considered in a more precise application of GCMs. These parameters are the role of clouds and the role of upwelling cold, deep ocean water.

If we start with a warming ocean surface the argument can be made that this warming would increase the amount of cloud cover. This increased cloud cover would make for a greater albedo for the planet, thereby decreasing the radiation reaching Earth's surface and tending to cool the surface. Aerosols, which are tiny sulfuric acid droplets found either in the stratosphere, from explosive volcanic eruptions like Pinatubo or Krakatoa, or in the troposphere from fossil fuel-derived sulfur dioxide emissions converting to sulfuric acid, reflect incoming sunlight and thereby decrease the radiant flux reaching the ground. Clouds and aerosols are poorly handled in most GCMs, therefore weakening their predictive capabilities. As these parameters are eventually introduced into the computer models with greater certainty the results will no doubt become more accurate.

A second parameter is the amount of cold water supplied to the surface ocean by upwelling. The deep oceans are the repositories of cold water and the time constant for the return of this cold water to the surface is about a thousand years. Therefore the surface oceans will always have a component supplied from the time when the cold deep water was formed. Attempts are being made to incorporate this term into the modeling but it is clear that the location, time, and intensity must be specified to obtain the most accurate results.

An attempt has been made to assess the consequences of global warming resulting from the increase in atmospheric CO_2 in a survey prepared for the U.S. Global Change Research Program of the Committee on Environment and Natural Resources Research of the federal government, published in 1995. Appendix 7–3 shows the probabilities of certain environmental changes inferred from the type of modeling discussed above. All such projections are, of course, subject to changes as new scientific data become available.

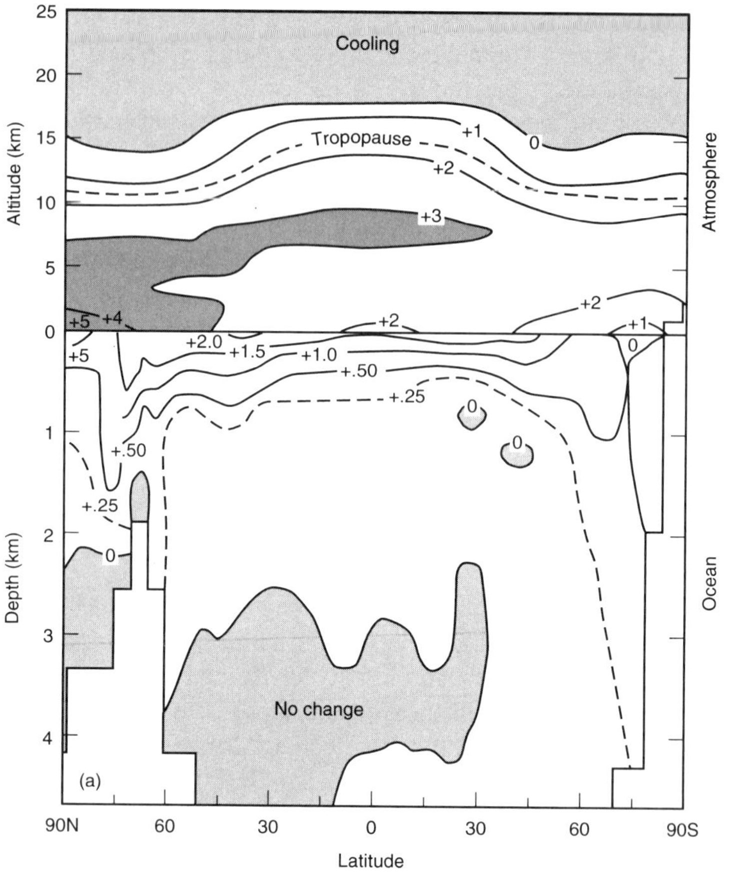

FIGURE 7–4 The changes in atmospheric and oceanic temperatures (in degrees Celsius) predicted by a general circulation model (GCM) for a doubling of the CO_2 concentration in the atmosphere from the present value based on a coupled ocean-atmosphere model. The projected doubling of CO_2 will occur in less than 100 years. Note that warming is not the same at all latitudes and that cooling occurs in the stratosphere. The major warming of the ocean is above 1 kilometer. (Modified after S. Manabe, R. J. Stouffer, and M. J. Spelman, 1994, *Ambio,* v. 23, p. 44.)

PROBLEM:

A. Methane (CH_4), also known as "marsh gas" and "natural gas," has been increasing in the atmosphere at an approximately constant rate between 1890 A.D. and 1990 A.D. (whereas for most of the previous 10,000 years the concentration was at the 1890 A.D. level). In 1890 A.D. the concentration was 0.7 ppmv and in 1990 A.D. it was 1.7 ppmv. Methane is destroyed in the atmosphere by reaction mainly with a chemical species (OH) formed by the dissociation of water as the result of sunlight. The mean life of methane in the atmosphere has been estimated to be 10 years.

Methane enters the atmosphere from a variety of sources. The equation describing the linear growth of methane in the atmosphere based on the flux of methane and the destruction of methane is

Rate of increase of CH_4 in the atmosphere =
Flux of methane as a function of time – Rate of loss in the atmosphere.

This is expressable by the equation

$$\Delta x/\Delta t = F_0 e^{\alpha t} - kx$$

where $\Delta x/\Delta t$ is the slope of methane growth with time, F_0 was the flux of methane to the atmosphere in 1890 A.D. (t = 0), k is the first order methane destruction constant (k is the reciprocal of the mean life of methane), x is the concentration of methane at any time t; $t = 0$ in 1890 A.D. and $t = 100$ in 1990 A.D., α is a measure of the way the flux of methane has been increasing since 1890 A.D..

1. What is the value of F_0 (ppmv per year)?
2. What is the value of α?
3. What was the flux ($= F_0 e^{\alpha t}$) of methane in 1990 A.D.?
4. If this equation is valid for the future, what will be the flux of methane to the atmosphere in 2090 A.D.?

B. The change in flux of methane over the past 100 years approximately matches the rate of increase in population. The sources of methane released to the atmosphere have been identified and their current relative roles estimated. These are:

- 20% fossil methane (coal and oil related)
- 20% rice paddies
- 20% ruminants (cows, sheep, etc.)
- 20% biomass burning (mainly continuously in Africa but also in the Amazon and elsewhere)
- 20% wetlands, termites, etc.

As methane is presently the third most important "greenhouse" gas (after H_2O and CO_2) and is becoming a more and more important component of the global warming component, what methods would you propose to attenuate the increase of methane in the atmosphere and what would you expect to be the social consequences?

APPENDIX 7–1: THE RELATIONSHIOP BETWEEN CO_2 IN THE ATMOSPHERE AND ACIDITY OF THE OCEAN[1]

The acidity of a solution is determined by the concentration of hydrogen ions (H^+). The water molecule, composed of hydrogen and oxygen, can form ions by dissociation much as the inorganic compounds or salts do when put into solution. For salts like sodium chloride the dissociation is complete for all practical purposes. The degree of dissociation of water, however, is far from complete. The dissociation of water is written

$$H_2O \text{ (liquid)} = H^+ \text{ (aqueous)} + OH^- \text{ (aqueous)}$$

The equilibrium product constant for this reaction is written in a manner similar to that for the solubility product constant

$$K_{\text{dissociation}} = [H^+][OH^-]$$

In pure water, for every hydrogen (H^+) ion formed by dissociation, a hydroxyl (OH^-) ion must be formed; the concentration of each is the same. The value of $K_{\text{dissociation}}$ at atmospheric pressure and 25°C is about 10^{-14}, hence the *hydrogen ion concentration* of pure water is 10^{-7}.

Commonly, purely as a matter of convenience, the hydrogen-ion concentration scale is converted to logarithmic form (base 10) to avoid writing exponents. Such a scale is called the *pH scale:* pH is defined as the negative logarithm of the hydrogen-ion concentration of 10^{-7} and is the pH of pure water. A lesser pH value is considered acidic, a greater one is basic. Since the pH of seawater is around 8, the ocean can be considered as a slightly basic solution.

In the laboratory, the pH of water can be lowered by adding an acid, such as hydrochloric acid or acetic acid (vinegar), since on dissociation it adds hydrogen ions without adding hydroxyl ions; pH can be raised by adding a base, such as sodium hydroxide (lye) or ammonium hydroxide (ammonia water).

The chemical species involved in the regulation of the pH of ocean water are also common compounds: carbon dioxide in the air, carbonic acid, and calcium carbonate. Carbon dioxide gas is the respiratory waste of animals and the starting point for photosynthesis in land plants. When carbon dioxide is bubbled through water, it dissolves to form carbonic acid, thus lowering the pH of the solution. This carbonic acid will react vigorously with calcium carbonate, with an increase in the pH. The reaction is

$$H_2CO_3 + CaCO_3 = Ca^{++} + 2HCO_3^-$$

It is evident that hydrogen ions from the dissociation of the carbonic acid are in part used up to form bicarbonate ions (HCO_3^-) from carbonate ions ($CO_3^=$) that are derived from the dissociation of the $CaCO_3$. This action tends to regulate the pH of the solution, hence we say the solution is "buffered." More precisely, the series of chemical reactions described above and their intermediate steps can be expressed in the following equations, shown with their associated equilibrium constants (including the dissociation constants and solubility product constants) at 25°C.

[1]From K. K. Turekian, 1976, *Oceans*, 2nd ed., Prentice Hall.

$K_p = 10^{-1.47}$ CO_2 (gas) + H_2O (liquid) = H_2CO_3 (aqueous)
$K_1 = 10^{-6.4}$ H_2CO_3 (aqueous) = H^+ (aqueous) + HCO_3^- (aqueous)
$K_2 = 10^{-10.3}$ HCO_3^- (aqueous) = H^+ (aqueous) + $CO_3^=$ (aqueous)
$K_{SP} = 10^{-8.3}$ $CaCO_3$ (solid) + H_2O (liquid) = Ca^{++} (aqueous) + $CO_3^=$ (aqueous)
$K_w = 10^{-14}$ H_2O (liquid) = H^+ (aqueous) + OH^- (aqueous)

On the basis of these equations and the dissociation of water, we can relaate the pressure of carbon dioxide in the atmosphere to the acidity of seawater on the basis of equilibrium with calcium carbonate, which is given by the following simplified equation:

$$P_{CO_2} = \left(K_p K_1\right)^{-1}\left(\frac{2K_{SP}}{K_2}\right)^{\frac{1}{2}}\left[H^+\right]^{\frac{1}{2}}$$

The present-day pressure of carbon dioxide is 0.0003 atmospheres, corresponding to a pH of about 8 for seawater, the value which is, in fact, found. Rather large changes in the carbon dioxide pressure result in only small change in the pH.

APPENDIX 7–2: EVIDENCE FOR A CHANGE IN THE CO_2 CONCENTRATION OF THE ATMOSPHERE ABOUT SEVEN MILLION YEARS AGO

Is there a direct measure of the decrease in the CO_2 content of the atmosphere of 7 million years ago? The answer is that although we may not yet have a way of getting the direct record of CO_2 in the air (that is, there are no ice cores going that far back in time), there are diagnostic properties in fossil remains that seem to point to a way of tracking the change.

The often used statement, "You are what you eat" has different meanings to different people, but according to one indicator there is scientific truth to the statement. That indicator is found in the relative abundances of the carbon isotopes ^{12}C and ^{13}C.

The basis of life in most places on Earth is photosynthesis, which transforms carbon dioxide and water to organic matter. The common plants effect this synthesis through one of two pathways. The Calvin cycle involves three-carbon compounds called phosphoglyceraldehydes whereas the Hatch-Slack cycle involves four-carbon phosphoglyceraldehydes. Plants using the Calvin cycle of photosynthesis are called C_3 plants and those using the Hatch-Slack cycle are called C_4 plants. The C_3 plants include all trees, wheat, barley, rice, and many other grains as well as bushes. The C_4 plants include maize ("corn"), sugar cane, sorghum, crabgrass, and the major component of prairie grass.

During photosynthesis the transformation of carbon dioxide results in the fractionation of the carbon isotopes ^{12}C, the most common, and ^{13}C, the other stable isotope. The differences are small but measurable with a mass spectrometer. The measurements are made and reported relative to a standard sample. This sample (PDB) happens to be the carbon in the calcium carbonate fossil test of a Cretaceous cephalopod called a belemnite that is found in the Peedee formation of South Carolina. As in the case of the oxygen isotopes, the differences from the standard are given in parts per thousand. That is

$$\left[\frac{\left({}^{13}C/{}^{12}C\right)\text{sample} - \left({}^{13}C/{}^{12}C\right)\text{standard}}{\left({}^{13}C/{}^{12}C\right)\text{standard}}\right] 1000 = \delta^{13}C$$

The $\delta^{13}C$ of atmospheric carbon dioxide is –7. C_3 plants have carbon with $\delta^{13}C$ of about –26 and C_4 plants –12.5. This difference is therefore diagnostic of the two types of plants. When plants are eaten by animals the muscle tissue isotopically directly records the type of plant eaten so that the transfer of this information can be seen through the animal food chain. The collagen fraction of bones, however, is enriched in the heavy isotope of carbon by about 5 parts per thousand over the food $\delta^{13}C$. The collagen, often preserved in fossil bones, then is a direct measure of the $\delta^{13}C$ of the food eaten, although "heavier" by 5 parts per thousand.

An animal (or humans) eating exclusively C_3 plants or the muscle tissue (flesh) of other animals eating only C_3 plants will have collagen in the bone with a $\delta^{13}C$ of –21 (the food is –26, the fractionation is +5) whereas the collagen of an animal in the C_4 food chain will be –7.5. Values between –21 and –7.5 indicate a mixed diet of C_3 and C_4 plants (or flesh) in that food chain.

There is clear evidence that the C_3 plants developed in environments reasonably well watered and at times with high atmospheric CO_2. In that way the environment resembles that of a contemporary florist's greenhouse where high humidity, high CO_2, and high temperature are desired nominal conditions. The nature of C_3 plants in photosynthesis is to be unconcerned about storing either CO_2 or H_2O (the necessities for photosynthesis) efficiently and so are best adapted to high-CO_2, high-humidity environments. The C_4 plants, on the other hand, are constructed to be conservative of both CO_2 and H_2O. They clearly have the advantage in low-CO_2 environments and are known to thrive relative to C_3 plants in water-stressed environments.

The analysis of the organic fraction of teeth of grazers, such as horses, worldwide during the past 10 million years indicates a sharp change in diet from predominantly C_3 grasses and other plants to C_4 plants about 7 million years ago (see Figure 7A–2). If we apply our criteria of dominance of C_4 grasses over C_3 grasses because of a drop in CO_2 in the atmosphere, we have a connection among mountain building, weathering, and decrease in atmospheric CO_2. The changes were undoubtedly going on as the Himalayas were forming but were exacerbated about 7 million years ago. Could this dropping CO_2 also have aided in the general cooling of Earth? Some scientists treat the decrease in CO_2, the drop in temperature, and the growth of ice as variables that eventually resulted in the wide oscillations in climate characteristic of the ice ages. These oscillations were then controlled by the externally controlled orbital Milankovitch cycle which acts as the "pacemaker of the ice ages."

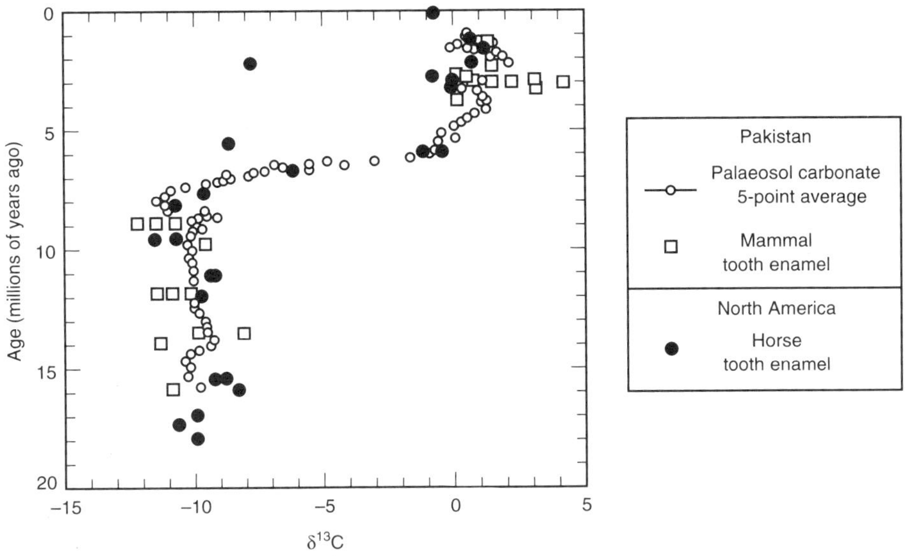

FIGURE 7A–2 The shift in $\delta^{13}C$ from light to heavy in tooth enamel of grazing animals and paleosols about 7 million years ago in North America and Pakistan. (After T. Cerling, Y. Wang, and J. Quade, 1993, *Nature,* v. 361, p. 344. Reprinted with permission, copyright Macmillan Magazines Limited.)

APPENDIX 7–3: POSSIBLE EFFECTS ON THE ENVIRONMENT INFERRED FROM CLIMATE MODELS[1]

Virtually Certain

1. Large stratospheric cooling will result from the increase in CO_2 concentration and ozone depletion; the start of such cooling has been predicted by models and observed in the upper stratosphere.

Very Probable

2. Global mean surface temperature warming will increase by the mid-twenty-first century. The best available estimate is that global mean surface temperatures will increase by about 0.5 to 2°C (or about 1 to 3.5°F) over the period from 1990 to 2050 due to increases in the concentrations of greenhouse gases alone (note that point 15 indicates it is inappropriate to convert these estimates to a per-decade basis), assuming no significant actions to reduce the projected increase in the rate of emissions of these gases. The best available estimate for a climate change that is in equilibrium with two times the pre-industrial carbon dioxide concentration

[1]From *U.S. Global Change Research Program Report 95-02,* July 1995, report chaired by E. Barron.

(or equivalent in terms of other greenhouse gases) is a warming of 1.5 to 4.5°C, with 2.5°C being the most probable estimate.

3. Global mean precipitation will increase. The distribution of this change is less certain.
4. Northern hemisphere sea ice will be reduced (the magnitude of the change will depend on the amount of the warming, and the reduced extent will initially be most evident in the transition seasons). Projected changes and their timing in the southern hemisphere sea-ice extent are less certain.
5. Arctic land areas will experience wintertime warming.
6. Global sea level will rise at an increasing rate, although with some probability that the rate of rise may not be significantly greater than at present. The most reasonable estimates for the rate of sea-level rise are for a rise of 5–40 cm by 2050, as compared to a rise of 5–12 cm if rates of rise over the past century continue.
7. Solar variability over the next 50 years will not induce a prolonged forcing that is significant in comparison with the effects of the increasing concentrations of CO_2 and other greenhouse gases.

Probable

8. Summer northern hemisphere mid-latitude continental dryness will increase.
9. High-latitude precipitation will increase, with potential feedback effects related to the influence of additional freshwater on the thermohaline circulation and of increased snowfall or rain on the mass balance of polar ice caps.
10. Antarctic and North Atlantic ocean regions will experience warming that is slower than the global average.
11. Transient explosive volcanic eruptions will result in short-term relative cooling.

Uncertain

12. Changes in climate variability will occur. As yet there is no clear evidence that suggests how the character of interannual variability may change due to greenhouse warming, but there is the potential for multifaceted and complicated, even counter-intuitive, changes in variability.
13. Regional scale (100–2000 km) climate changes will be different from the global average changes. However, at present there is only very limited capability to estimate how various regions will respond to global climate change.
14. Tropical storm intensity may change.
15. Details of the climate change over the next 25 years are uncertain.
16. Biosphere-climate feedbacks are expected, but how much these feedbacks will amplify or moderate climate change is uncertain.

8

CHLORINATED FLUOROCARBONS (CFCs) AND STRATOSPHERIC OZONE

Carbon dioxide, methane, and the chemical components of acid rain occur at some level naturally in the atmosphere. Their concentrations have increased because of anthropogenic loadings. Humans, however, have been responsible uniquely for introducing a set of compounds to the atmosphere that had never existed there before and that have significant capacities for altering the environment. These compounds collectively are called chlorinated fluorocarbons or CFCs. They include the well-known freon compounds used as refrigerants. The CFCs are stable to destruction in the troposphere. They have low solubilities in water and are not easily destroyed biologically. It is only when they reach the stratosphere that they are decomposed to chlorine and fluorine compounds such as HCl and HF. These molecules are also naturally present to some degree in the atmosphere but the increase in the stratosphere is mainly due to the decomposition of CFCs. The mechanism of destruction is the interaction with the ultraviolet component of the sun's rays. Much of the ultraviolet flux to Earth's surface is strongly attenuated by reactions with a variety of molecules in the stratosphere. The transformation of CFCs to simple molecules of chlorine and fluorine occurs almost exclusively in the stratosphere. The increase of CFCs in the atmosphere and the consequent increase of the concentrations of their degradation products in the stratosphere result in a marked change in stratospheric chemistry. This change in CFC-degradation products must be linked in some way to the alteration of the chemistry of other chemical species in the stratosphere. In particular the effect on ozone

(O_3) has been of considerable interest because of the consequences to living beings on Earth.

THE OZONE SHIELD

Ozone is formed in the stratosphere by ultraviolet radiation from the sun. The short wavelength component of the ultraviolet rays is effective in tearing apart the common oxygen molecules (O_2) in the atmosphere. The newly freed oxygen then reacts with the normal O_2 molecules to form ozone. The equations describing the production process are written

$$O_2 + h\nu \rightarrow O + O$$

and

$$O + O_2 \rightarrow O_3$$

The energy of the reactive light ray, or photon, is designated $h\nu$, where h is a constant which transforms the frequency, ν, of the characteristic light into the specific energy of the photon necessary to break apart the O_2 molecule. (The frequency of a light ray is equal to the speed of light divided by the wavelength. The shorter the wavelength, the higher the frequency and therefore the higher the energy of the photon.)

Ozone, once created, has the property of absorbing ultraviolet radiation capable of reaching Earth's surface that is most harmful to living matter (called UV-B, with a wavelength of around 300 nanometers). The existence of ozone, then, permits organisms to exist at Earth's surface in habitats that expose them to the direct rays of the sun. Without the ozone "shield," early in Earth's history, microorganisms survived perhaps by living in shielded environments such as translucent calcareous and siliceous coverings or by developing efficient cellular healing strategies as some bacteria have at the present time. Only as oxygen built up in the atmosphere could the ozone shield develop and thus allow greater mobility and occupation of Earth's surface by evolving organisms.

The creation of ozone in the stratosphere is followed by its destruction. Normally the process of destruction is through two mechanisms: (1) Ozone absorbs ultraviolet radiation having a wavelength of about 300 nanometers and the molecule thereby dissociates to ordinary O_2. This wavelength has the energy that most strongly destroys DNA in living matter. The act of absorption of this wavelength by ozone diminishes its flux to Earth's surface, thereby protecting life. (2) Ozone is also destroyed by chemical reactions with molecules in the stratosphere produced from the destruction of methane (CH_4) and nitrous oxide (N_2O) having their source in the troposphere. (These reactions are discussed in detail in Appendix 8–1.)

Obviously, variations in the solar flux will control both the production and destruction of ozone. Also, variations in the amounts of methane and nitrous oxide transferred from the troposphere to the stratosphere will influence the destruction rate of ozone in the stratosphere through the actions of their degradation products. The size of the reservoir of ozone in the stratosphere depends on the sum of the rates of destruction of ozone, since the production rate is fixed by the solar flux acting on oxygen which is virtually invariant in concentration. As the total rate of destruction increases, the amount of ozone in the stratosphere decreases and the flux of biologically interactive ultraviolet light increases.

CHANGES IN THE OZONE CONCENTRATION IN THE STRATOSPHERE OVER TIME

The amount of ozone in the stratosphere varies naturally by season, by latitude, and by interannual variations in the sun's output of radiation. Generally this solar flux swing follows the approximately eleven-year sunspot cycles discussed earlier. During the summer of each hemisphere in the high latitudes, the long pathway of the sun's rays results in more ozone production than at low latitudes where the sun's rays are direct and traverse a shorter path through the stratosphere (Fig. 8–1). Conversely, during the long night of the polar winter at the high latitudes, virtually no ozone is produced, but none is destroyed either until the polar spring arrives. During the dark winter months in each hemisphere, the ozone levels in the Antarctic and Arctic stratospheres are maintained by supply from the lower latitudes and long distance from the sunlit hemisphere (Fig. 8–2).

The sharp change in solar radiance between seasons at Antarctica provides an arena to study photon-induced reactions and the consequences on stratospheric chemistry. At the British Antarctic Survey Station at Halley Bay in Antarctica (77°S latitude), continuous measurements on total ozone were made beginning in 1958. The data showed that each year in the austral spring (September) there was a dip in the ozone concentration as the sun's rays first appeared. The dip in ozone, soon to be called the "Antarctic ozone hole" in the popular press, deepened each succeeding year (Fig. 8–3). Satellite data over the past twenty years have corroborated the existence of this annual and deepening event.

Naturally, interest ran high in the possible causes of a clearly observed phenomenon for which no explanation was known. The decrease in solar radiance, progressive changes in exchange of stratospheric air over Antarctica with air farther north, or a chemical change in the stratosphere that specifically affected the production or destruction of ozone are three possible reasons for this phenomenon.

Measurements and theoretical calculations show that neither the change in radiance nor latitudinal transport processes are adequate to explain

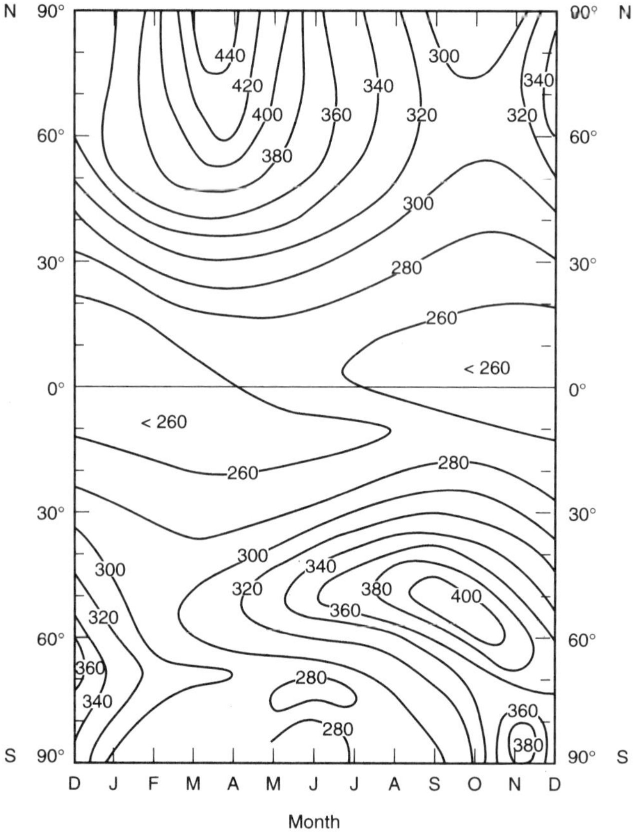

FIGURE 8–1 Column abundances of ozone as a function of latitude and month. The abundances are expressed in Dobson units; 1 DU = 2.69×10^{16} molecules O_3 cm^{-2}; 100 Dobson units corresponds to an ozone layer thickness of 1 mm if all ozone in a vertical column were at 1 atmosphere pressure and 0°C. (As summarized from various sources by H. U. Dütsch, 1971, *Advances in Geophysics,* v. 35, p. 29.)

the strong deepening of the Antarctic ozone hole, thus we are left with the chemical reactions in the stratosphere. In particular, the role of chlorine set free by the decomposition of CFCs began to be taken seriously because the ozone loss problem and the increasing release of CFCs had occurred in concert.

CHLORINATED FLUOROCARBONS (CFCs) AND THE ANTARCTIC OZONE HOLE

After a CFC molecule reaches the stratosphere it is transported upward where it eventually is photodissociated by ultraviolet light from the sun. This

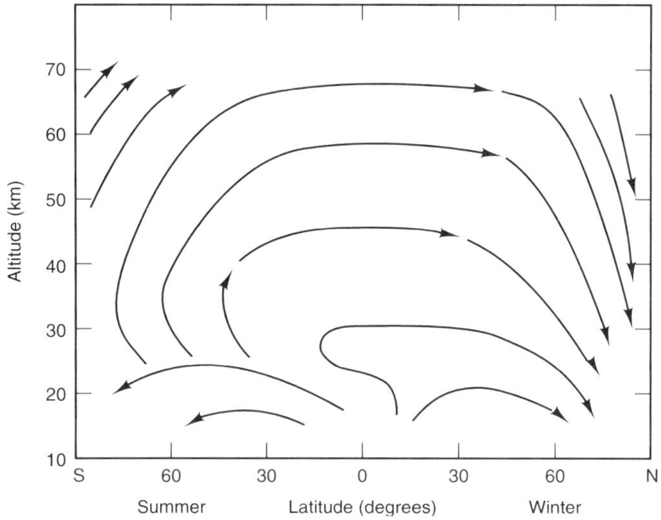

FIGURE 8–2 Flow lines in the stratosphere during heating in the southern hemisphere. The lower stratosphere resembles the Hadley circulation of the troposphere. The upper stratosphere transports air virtually from pole to pole. (After T. Dunkerton, 1978, *J. Atm. Sci.,* v. 35, p. 2325. American Meteorological Society.)

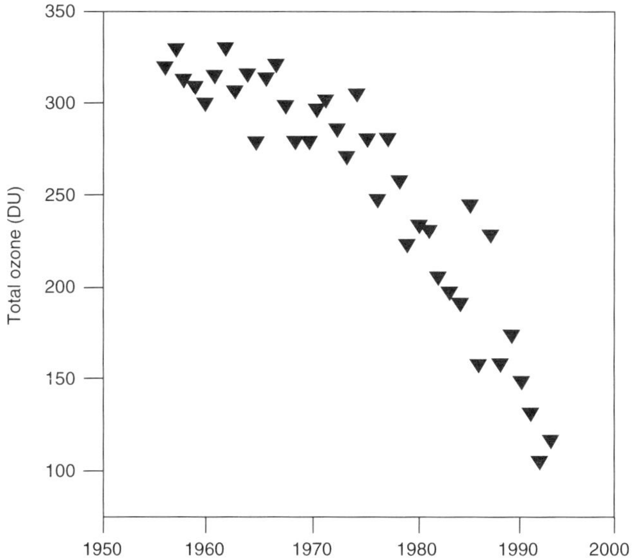

FIGURE 8–3 Monthly means and ranges of total ozone over Halley Bay, Antarctica, for October of the years 1957 through 1994. (Adapted from J. C. Farman, B. G. Gardiner, and J. D. Shanklin, 1985, *Nature,* v. 315, p. 207, and A. E. Jones and J. D. Shanklin, 1995, *Nature,* v. 376, p. 409. Reprinted with permission, copyright Macmillan Magazines Limited.)

dissociation in the presence of the OH radical (the same radical that is involved in the oxidation of methane) produces active Cl. The free Cl is immediately used in two reactions to produce HCl (hydrogen chloride) and ClO (chloroxide), both molecules more stable than free Cl. The formation of ClO is the reaction that is responsible for the destruction of ozone. The ClO molecule that is formed then reacts with NO_2 in the stratosphere to make $ClONO_2$. The main "reservoir" molecules for Cl are therefore HCl and $ClONO_2$. As the Cl atom is required for the destruction of ozone, the tapping of the reservoir molecules for free Cl becomes the limiting step to the rate of destruction of O_3.

The Antarctic region provides a special environment for the efficient destruction of ozone. During the Antarctic winter the air over Antarctica is drastically cooled and maintained as a vortex by strong circumantarctic winds. The column of air over Antarctica is then isolated and as it cools its density increases and it descends toward the surface. The tropopause is lowered and because of the very cold and high density conditions of the stratosphere air, condensation of crystals from gases begins to occur. Under these conditions it is the formation of the nitric acid trihydrate (and possibly other hydrates) crystals that is critical. These ice crystals act to occlude HCl. The gaseous $ClONO_2$ reacts with the occluded HCl to form free Cl and nitric acid, which then forms more crystals. The Cl atoms combine to form the stable Cl_2 molecule under dark conditions. When sunlight appears in the Antarctic spring, Cl_2 is dissociated and the free Cl reacts with the ozone, stored all winter long in the dark Antarctic, to form ClO. The details of the reactions are given in Appendix 8–2. As the amount of available Cl, due to the increase of CFCs, increases so does the efficiency of destroying ozone increase in the Antarctic spring.

WORLDWIDE OZONE DEPLETION

The mechanism for the generation of the Antarctic ozone hole has been effectively worked out and the dependence on the availability of chlorine (and bromine, as it turns out) established. Can this mechanism be invoked for the globe as a whole? The answer is ambiguous. Recently in the Arctic, the presence of significant ClO in the stratosphere has been established. This implies that the process of ozone destruction is possible in the Arctic, although not as easily attained as in the colder Antarctic vortex. Every once in a while the Arctic region develops a polar vortex like that found at Antarctica. In such a case the ozone level in the Arctic also decreases. The frequency of such events is not known and may be as few as two or three a century. There obviously is a more sustained way of diminishing ozone in the northern hemisphere. One method is to diminish the concentration of NO_2, thereby decreasing the probability of forming $ClONO_2$ which ties up much of the reactive chlorine. This is accomplished on the sulfate aerosol layer in the stratosphere resulting from the frequent supply of SO_2 to the stratosphere from Earth's many explosive volcanoes especially found in the northern hemisphere. Nitric acid is produced on these aerosol surfaces and is then removed by precipitation. This chain of events diminishes the NO_2 content of the stratosphere, thereby inhibiting the formation of $ClONO_2$ from ClO—the molecule involved in the ozone-destruction process. Thus there may be a relationship between large volcanic eruptions and even greater loss of ozone in any particular year. This seems to have been the case in 1992, a little less than a year after the explosion of Pinatubo.

Despite the suggested models for ozone destruction in the northern hemisphere, it is true that we have not yet attained the degree of certainty of this process as we have for the Antarctic polar vortex. Research is proceeding at such a rapid rate in this area that the actual northern hemisphere mechanism for ozone loss will undoubtedly soon be elucidated. At lower latitudes, where the temperature of the stratosphere is not sufficiently low to activate the Antarctic-type sequence of events of ozone destruction, the other mechanisms involving chlorine are considerably less efficient. Yet, the evidence suggests that the global inventory of stratospheric ozone is decreasing (Fig. 8–4).

CONSEQUENCES OF OZONE DEPLETION

Ozone is perennially created and destroyed in the stratosphere. The most important cycle involves the direct production of ozone from O_2 at one wavelength of ultraviolet light and its destruction at another wavelength (300 nm, the UV-B wavelength). The remaining reactions at the present time involve molecules (or atoms) of chlorine, nitrogen oxides, and hydrogen oxide. Changes in the abundances of any of these reactants will affect the thickness of the ozone shield. Nitrogen oxides are provided by the transport of nitrous oxide (N_2O), probably derived at present from fertilized agricultural fields, and hydrogen oxide is from the destruction of methane in the stratosphere (methane production also has a large agricultural component). Most of the chlorine, on the other hand, is derived from CFCs reaching the stratosphere. Large fluxes of HCl from volcanoes and methyl chloride from biological activity in the oceans are also supplied to the atmosphere but these materials are effectively transformed and removed in the troposphere and do not reach the stratosphere.

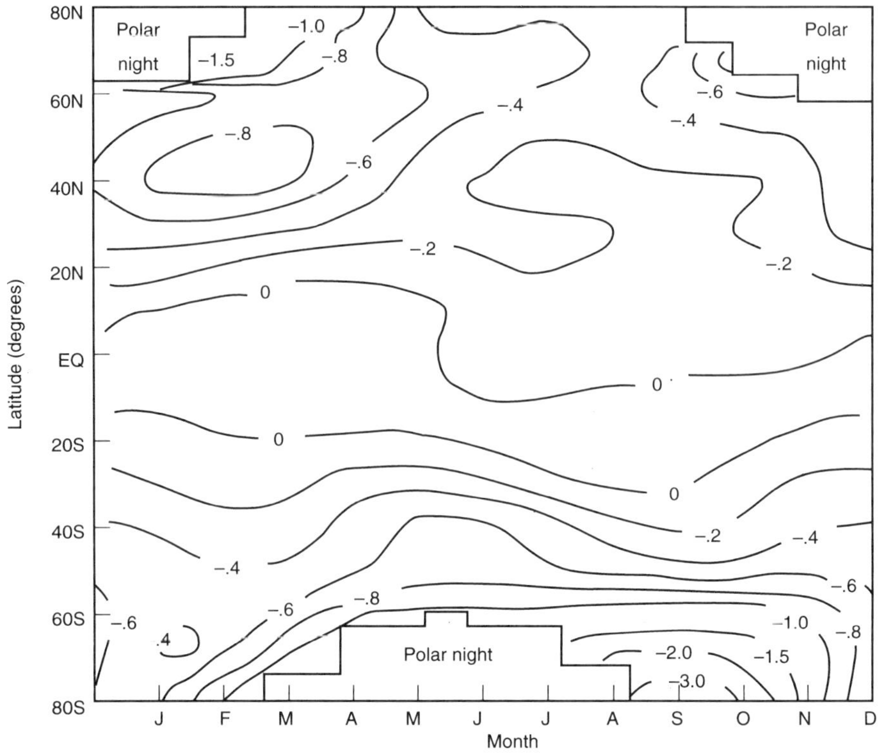

FIGURE 8–4 The change in total column ozone in percentage per year as a function of latitude and season for the period 1978–1990 as measured by the total ozone mapping spectrometer (TOMS) instrument on the Nimbus 7 satellite. The data are averaged over all longitudes. Data were not collected during the polar nights. (After R. S. Stolarski, P. Bloomfield, R. D. McPeters, and J. R. Herman, 1991, *Geophys. Res. Letters,* v. 18, p. 1015. Copyright American Geophysical Union.)

The significance of the ozone shield to life on Earth is clear (Fig. 8–5). Excessive exposure of humans to biologically active ultraviolet light (called UV-B) is known to cause skin cancers to those susceptible to it. Our changing lifestyle has increased the number of people exposed to sunlight, so that even without the ozone depletion effect the incidence of skin cancers has been increasing.

Actual increases in UV-B, the biologically active ultraviolet rays, have now been measured for at least two locations and have been related to ozone decrease. In the Antarctic (Fig. 8–6), a comparison of the irradiance in the ultraviolet between 1988 and 1990 clearly shows that the shorter wavelength ultraviolet rays, the ones absorbed by O_3 and harmful to life, have increased,

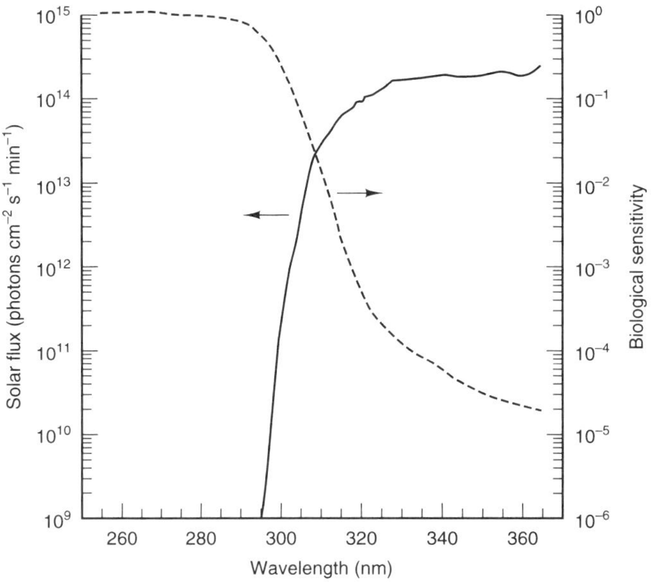

FIGURE 8–5 A comparison of the spectral flux of solar radiation reaching Earth's surface with the spectral sensitivity of biological organisms to radiation. The solid line shows the solar irradiance (scale at left) reaching Earth's surface when the sun is at a zenith angle of 39°. The dashed line shows biological sensitivity (scale at right) to radiation at different wavelengths. (The sensitivity parameter is the inverse ratio of the efficiency of absorption of solar radiation at a specified wavelength by DNA compared with the absorption by DNA of radiation with a wavelength of 260 nm.) Decreases in stratospheric ozone result in increases in irradiance in the wavelength region between 290 and 320 nm. (Figure supplied by C. Brühl, Max-Planck-Institut für Chemie, Mainz, Germany, to T. Graedel and P. Crutzen and appears with the above caption in their 1993 book, *Atmospheric Change*, W.H. Freeman Company; copyright by AT&T and used with permission.)

while the longer wavelength rays have stayed the same. A study in Toronto, Canada, shows a similar trend from 1988 to 1993 (Fig. 8–7).

These arguments give compelling reasons to worry about the decrease in stratospheric ozone over time. The nations of the world have agreed to decrease the production and use of CFCs over the next decade and eventually to phase out their use. The replacement products have been shown to be destroyed effectively in the troposphere and therefore will not affect the stratospheric ozone layer. This resolve has been codified in the "Montreal

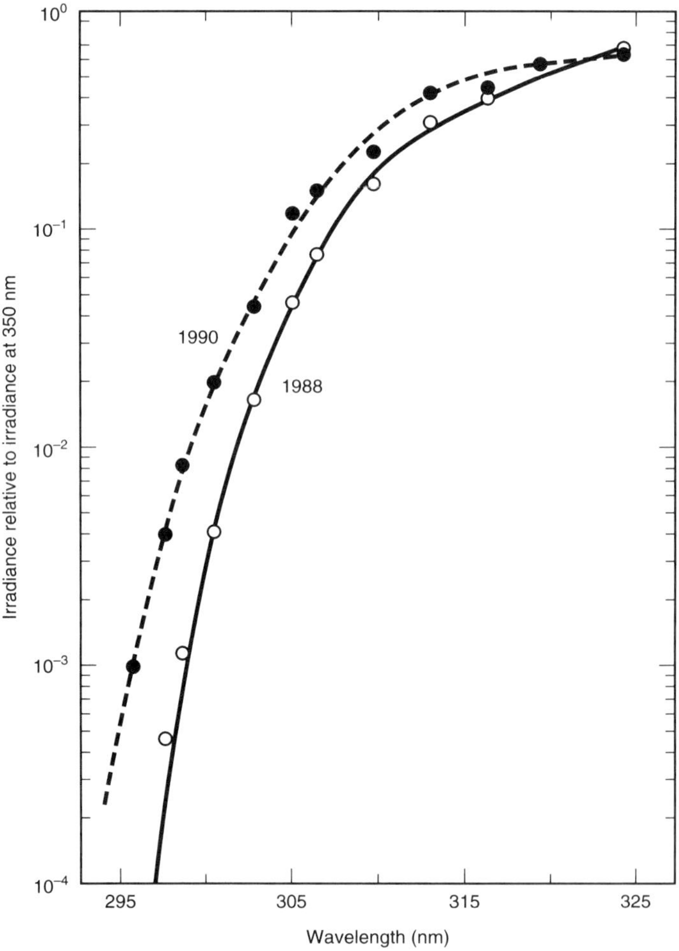

FIGURE 8–6 Ground-level irradiance ratio at Palmer Station, Antarctica. The data are for local noon on December 21, the austral summer solstice, in 1988 (solid line) and 1990 (dashed line). (From J. E. Frederick and A. D. Alberts, 1991, *Geophys. Res. Letters,* v. 18, p. 1869.)

Protocol on Substances That Deplete the Ozone Layer," most recently revised in 1992.

The ozone depletion problem differs from the global warming problem in that the reactions involved in ozone production and destruction are reasonably well known and alternatives to CFCs now exist on a commercial basis, while the details of the effects of the CO_2 increase and the potential of global warming are under intense scientific, economic, and political debate.

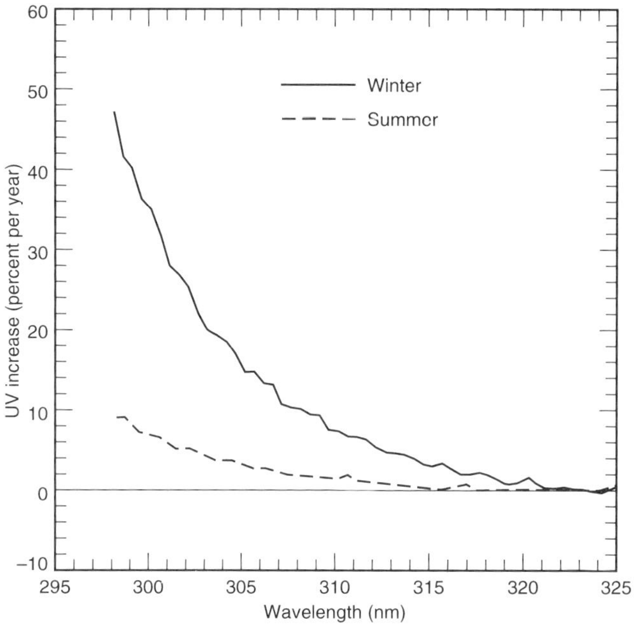

FIGURE 8–7 The increase in UV-B (~300 nanometers) in Toronto, Canada, between 1989 and 1993. The percent increase of UV per year is less as one proceeds from around 300 nm to 325 nm. The increase in UV-B (~300 nm) matches the measured decrease in stratospheric ozone at Toronto over the same time period. The longer wavelength radiation is not affected by ozone, therefore its flux will not change with time. (Reprinted with permission from J. Kerr and T. McElroy, 1993, *Science,* v. 262, p. 1032. Copyright American Association for the Advancement of Science.)

PROBLEM:

The critical step for the destruction of stratospheric ozone, beyond the normal processes, involves the role of increased availability of reactive chlorine in the atmosphere. What roles do methane and nitrous oxide supply to the atmosphere play in the survival or destruction of stratospheric ozone?

APPENDIX 8–1: CHEMICAL REACTIONS IN THE STRATOSPHERE AND THE CONTROLS ON OZONE DESTRUCTION

The roles of the "natural" molecules reaching the stratosphere are agents, ultimately, of the destruction of ozone. Methane is subject to attack by some of the free energetic oxygen atoms produced by the interaction of photons with O_2 molecules. These energetic oxygen atoms react with methane to produce other molecules such as OH, H_2O, and CO_2. The OH is an unstable, highly reactive molecule and enters into a number of additional reactions in the stratosphere that influence the fate of O_3. The reactions for the destruction of ozone involving OH are

$$OH + O_3 \rightarrow HO_2 + O_2$$
$$HO_2 + O_3 \rightarrow OH + 2O_2$$

so that two O_3 molecules are converted to three O_2 molecules with OH acting as a catalyst. As a catalyst it enters into the reaction to effect the destruction of ozone, but the total amount of OH itself is not changed. So, through this pathway we can say that methane can join in the destruction of ozone. As the flux of anthropogenic methane has been increasing over time (see Chapter 7) there is undoubtedly an effect on the survival of ozone, although not as large as some other reactions we now discuss.

Nitrous oxide reaching the stratosphere from the troposphere is oxidized to the nitric oxides NO and NO_2. Ozone is destroyed by reactions involving these oxides.

$$NO + O_3 \rightarrow NO_2 + O_2$$
$$NO_2 + O \rightarrow NO + O_2$$

The concentrations of NO and NO_2 are maintained and one ozone and one free energetic oxygen are destroyed to produce two O_2 in the sum of the above reactions. The nitrogen pathway therefore also acts to destroy ozone. Incidentally, NO and NO_2 are very quickly removed from the troposphere. The only way that these molecules exist in the stratosphere is through the oxidation of N_2O transferred from the troposphere. Nitrous oxide (N_2O) is very stable in the troposphere. There is evidence that, because of the increasing use of fertilizers, there is also an increase in N_2O supplied to the atmosphere so that N_2O joins CH_4 as anthropogenically enhanced molecules aiding in the destruction of ozone.

APPENDIX 8–2: THE OZONE HOLE OVER ANTARCTICA

After CFC reaches the stratosphere it is transported upward where it eventually is photodissociated by ultraviolet light from the sun. This dissociation in the presence of the OH radical produces active Cl in the following way:

$$CFC + h\nu \xrightarrow{OH} Cl + HF + CO_2$$

The free Cl is immediately used in two reactions:

(1) $$Cl + CH_4 \rightarrow HCl + CH_3$$

(CH_3 then reacts with OH to form $CO_2 + H_2O$)

(2) $$Cl + O_3 \rightarrow ClO + O_2$$

The presence of NO_2 in the stratosphere ultimately from the oxidation of N_2O acts to convert ClO to $ClONO_2$ by the reaction

$$ClO + NO_2 \rightarrow ClONO_2$$

The main "reservoir" molecules for Cl are therefore HCl and $ClONO_2$.

As Cl is required for the destruction of ozone (as one of the agents), the tapping of the reservoir molecules for free Cl becomes the limiting step to the rate of destruction of O_3.

The Antarctic region provides a peculiarly special environment for the efficient destruction of ozone as the result of Cl supplied by the photodissociation of CFC. During the Antarctic winter the air over Antarctica is drastically cooled and maintained as a vortex by strong circumantarctic winds. The column of air over Antarctica is then isolated and as it cools it descends toward the surface. The tropopause is lowered and condensation of gases in the stratosphere begins to occur.

Water exists in the stratosphere as the result of the oxidation of methane (CH_4). The nitrogen-bearing compounds all got started as N_2O. Both CH_4 and N_2O are derived from the surface of Earth as a result of biological activity. NO_2, formed by the oxidation of N_2O, reacts with OH, formed by the dissociation of H_2O, to form nitric acid, $HONO_2$

$$NO_2 + OH \rightarrow HONO_2$$

At the very cold temperatures of the dark Antarctic polar vortex in winter (our northern hemisphere summer), gaseous $HONO_2$ and H_2O form crystals of $HONO_2 \cdot 3H_2O$, that is, nitric acid trihydrate. The crystals are as large as 1 to 3 micrometers in size. The crystals condense HCl, one of the Cl reservoir gases, with them.

The crystals then become the sites of further reactions involving the other reservoir gas for Cl, $ClONO_2$, by the reaction with the occluded HCl in the nitric acid trihydrate ice crystals:

$$ClONO_2\ (\text{gas}) + HCl\ (\text{in ice crystal}) = HONO_2\ (\text{combining with water to increase the crystal size}) + Cl_2\ (\text{gas})$$

So all during the Antarctic winter, Cl_2 (the stable form of chlorine in the absence of photodissociation) accumulates in the atmosphere.

At dawn in Antarctica in September this Cl_2 is photodissociated:

$$Cl_2 + h\nu \rightarrow Cl + Cl$$

The destruction of O_3 then begins in earnest through the chlorine pathway.

This pathway is considered a catalytic reaction in which ClO is conserved (actually it is destroyed and reconstructed—it just seems like nothing happened to it). The following set of reactions occurs:

$$Cl + O_3 \rightarrow ClO + O_2$$

$$ClO + ClO \rightarrow ClO\ OCl$$

$$ClO\ OCl + h\nu \rightarrow Cl + ClO\ O$$

$$ClO\ O + M \rightarrow Cl + O_2 + M$$

$$Cl + O_3 \rightarrow ClO + O_2$$

(M is another molecule that acts to absorb the excess energy.)

The net reaction therefore results in

$$2O_3 \rightarrow 3O_2$$

The simplified reaction first proposed,

$$Cl + O_3 \rightarrow ClO + O_2$$
$$ClO + O \rightarrow Cl + O2$$

does not appear to be correct for the Antarctic situation.

The unique role of Antarctic air as the site of ozone destruction from thc Cl produced from CFC arises from the formation of the nitric acid trihydrate crystals with occluded HCl. This process provides a way of releasing chlorine from the two reservoir gases $ClONO_2$ and HCl. Only then is the role of chlorine as an ozone-destruction agent satisfied.

9

ACID RAIN AND TROPOSPHERIC OZONE

So far our discussion of changes in atmospheric composition has focused on global consequences. Although the release of carbon dioxide, methane, nitrous oxide, and CFCs is mainly in the northern hemisphere, their effects are global because of the relatively rapid transfer of air between hemispheres in both the troposphere and the stratosphere.

Other gases emitted to the atmosphere have short life times and therefore cause regional effects. These gases include sulfur dioxide and other sulfur-bearing gaseous compounds, the nitric oxides NO and NO_2 (together commonly called NO_x), and volatile organic compounds (commonly written in shorthand fashion as VOC). These gases have both natural and anthropogenic components. It is the human-accelerated release of these compounds that has increased acid rain deposition and tropospheric ozone formation. The consequences of these emissions to global environmental changes as well as regional changes are discussed in the following sections.

SULFUR AND NITROGEN COMPOUND EMISSIONS AND ACID RAIN

Almost anywhere in the world atmospheric precipitation is acidic. A pH of about 5.8 (where 7 is neutral) in precipitation is maintained under natural conditions by the solution of atmospheric carbon dioxide in the precipitation. The acidity of club soda or sparkling water from certain springs is due to the same phenomenon except that higher pressures of carbon dioxide are involved. There are, however, other kinds of gases reacting with precipitation that lower the pH even more than carbon dioxide. These gases include sulfur dioxide (SO_2) and the nitric oxides. When these sulfur and nitrogen compounds dissolve in precipitation and are oxidized they form the strong acids, sulfuric acid and nitric acid. Sometimes these acids are neutralized in the rain droplets by reaction with dust made of calcium carbonate or other acid-neutralizing soluble species such as ammonia. If neutralization does not occur, the precipitation falling on the ground remains acidic. Eventually reactions with soils and rocks will neutralize the water and the pH of streams and groundwaters are then determined by other processes such as biological activity, and the pH of the original precipitation is no longer observed.

If the capacity for neutralization at Earth's surface is not great enough locally and the water collects in lakes, the properties of the lake will reflect this acidity. The observation of the acidification of some lakes and experiments on the response of certain plants to acid precipitation has led to a concern about human-accelerated changes in the production of the precursor gases responsible for acid rain and the resiliency of nature to this increased burden.

There are natural sources of volatile sulfur delivered to the atmosphere (Table 9–1). Volcanic eruptions provide sulfur dioxide both to the troposphere and the stratosphere. The effect in the troposphere is small compared to both the anthropogenic emissions and the other natural source—biotic. Marine organisms manufacture and release volatile sulfur-bearing compounds that are responsible in large part for the "smell of the sea." Compounds such as dimethyl sulfide, on escape from the ocean surface to the atmosphere, are quickly converted to precursors of sulfuric acid rain. Some volatile organic compounds such as carbonyl sulfide are sufficiently resistant to destruction in the troposphere that they move ultimately to the stratosphere. There they are transformed into the usual oxygen-bearing compounds of sulfur. At present the volatile sulfur flux from marine biotic sources is secondary in importance to the anthropogenic flux of SO_2, but regionally the natural marine biotic source may be the dominant source of acid rain. Such regions are areas of high biological productivity associated with ocean upwelling or areas of coastal pollution.

The anthropogenic source of sulfur dioxide gas is the burning of sulfur-rich fossil fuels, mainly for the production of electric energy. In coals, sulfur exists as iron sulfide minerals such as pyrite ("fool's gold") and as sulfur-rich organic compounds constituting the fabric of coal. The latter occurrence is also typical of high-sulfur oil. When fossil fuel is burned, the reaction with oxygen produces carbon dioxide as it generates energy. In the process, in sulfur-bearing fuels, gaseous sulfur dioxide is formed which escapes into the atmosphere with the carbon dioxide. Some coals and oils

TABLE 9–1: Estimates of Natural Sulfur Emissions (in Tg S yr^{-1})*

	SO_2	H_2S	COS	DMS	CS_2	Sulfate	Other	Total
Sea spray						38–320		38–320
Dust						3–32		3–32
Total particulates						41–352		41–352
Volcanoes	7.4–9.3	1.0	0.010	-	0.010	<3	?	10–13
Soils and plants	-	3.0–10	0.2–0.6	0.2–4	0.6–0.8	-	1	5–13
Coastal wetlands	-	1.0	0.1	0.6	0.06	-	0.1	1.9
Biomass burning	2.6	?	0.1	-	?	?	?	≥2.6
Oceans (gases)	-	1.6–6.4	0.4	19–51	0.3	-	?	35–58
Total gases	10.0–13	6.0–19	1.0–1.3	19–54	1.0–1.3	≤3	1	38–89

*Teragram (Tg) is equal to 10^{12} grams.

are more enriched in sulfur than others. The air containing the sulfur dioxide gas distributes the potential acid rain along the direction of the major wind patterns. Only as the sulfur dioxide gas is transformed to sulfuric acid by oxidation is there an acid effect. This oxidation occurs both in the air, in rain droplets, and by reaction with the damp surfaces of ground level such as vegetation. Approximately half of the sulfur dioxide is transformed to sulfuric acid in several days so that the rapidly moving air distributes the acid rain potentially thousands of miles "downwind" of the source of sulfur dioxide production.

The high-sulfur coals in the United States are mined and burned in the midwestern states to a large degree. The main air patterns transport the sulfur dioxide eastward toward eastern Canada and the northeastern United States with a travel time of one to two days. All along the way additional sulfur dioxide is added to the air from power plants. The concentration of sulfur dioxide and the conversion to acid rain is most pronounced in these eastern regions as the result of these processes (Fig. 9–1).

The amount of sulfur dioxide released to the air by power plants can be diminished by physically removing the sulfur in minerals, such as pyrite, prior to burning. The only efficient way of removing sulfur dioxide produced by the incineration of the organically bound sulfur in coal and oil is to use "scrubbers" in the stacks. These scrubbers are composed of fluidized beds of calcium carbonate (or limestone) which is converted to calcium sulfate with the release of carbon dioxide. Treaties with Canada and the regulatory requirements within the United States are in force to decrease the total amount of sulfur dioxide released to the atmosphere. Until we realize the importance of diminishing the amount of organic sulfur burned and until we understand the value and feasibility of scrubbing, sulfur dioxide will be released, to some extent, to the atmosphere by fossil fuel-fired power plants.

Gaseous sulfur dioxide is oxidized to sulfate through three processes. About a third of the sulfate in precipitation is produced by reactions in clouds (or rain droplets) involving the dissolving of SO_2 in water droplets that also dissolve hydrogen peroxide produced in polluted atmospheres. These react to produce sulfuric acid. The remaining sulfate found in precipitation comes from aerosols produced by the molecular collisions of SO_2 gas molecules and the hydroxyl (OH) molecule produced by sunlight acting on water vapor. These aerosols act as nuclei for the formation of rain droplets. Sulfate aerosols act to increase the albedo of the planet in the troposphere as the volcanically derived aerosols do in the stratosphere. But in the troposphere, as nucleating agents for cloud droplets, their role in thickening clouds and increasing the albedo in this manner may be more important. In any case, the

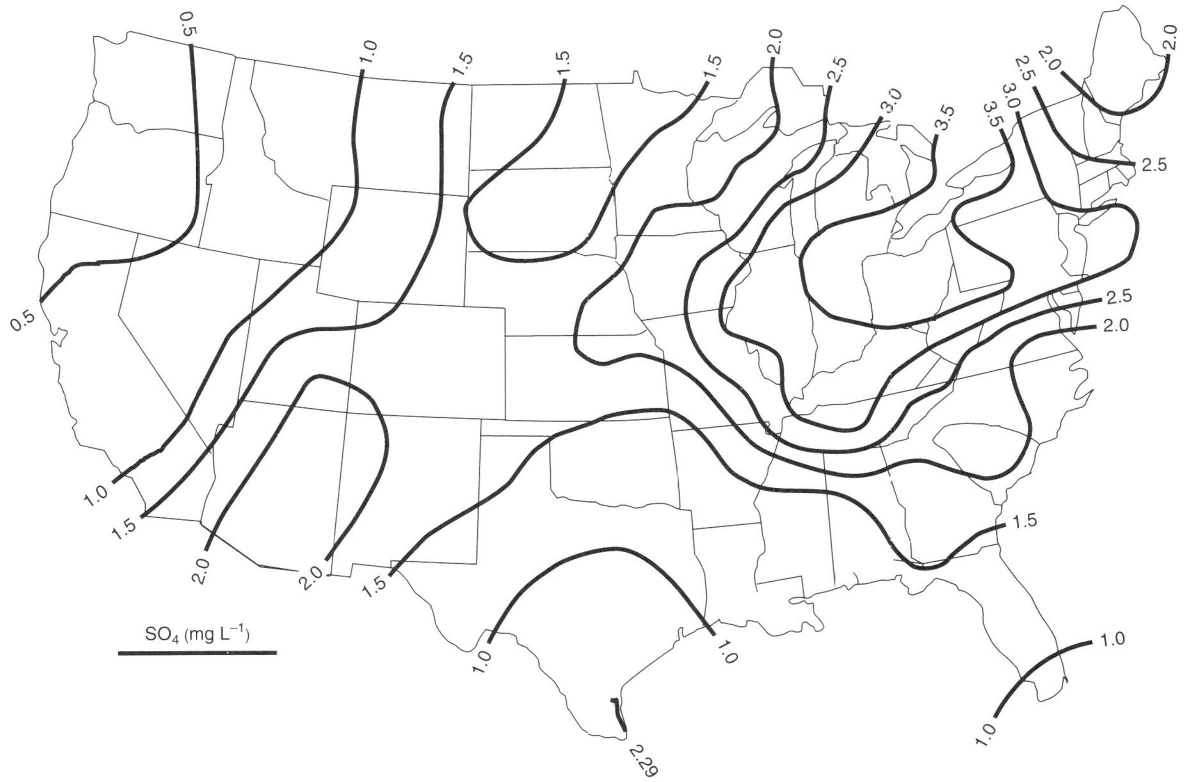

FIGURE 9–1 Weighted-average sulfate concentration in precipitation (milligrams per liter) during 1978–1981. (Summary from National Research Council Report, *Acid Deposition*, 1986, National Academy Press.)

decrease of radiation to the lower troposphere acts to cool it. The cooling effect may match the warming expected by the addition of CO_2 by fossil fuel burning according to some scientists, thereby giving a smaller net effect of warming than expected from the addition of CO_2 alone.

Note, however, that the sulfate remains airborne in the atmosphere with a mean life of five days, whereas CO_2 is in the atmosphere as a gas with a mean life of ten years or more. Thus if we clean up sulfur from power plant emissions, the CO_2 effect will increase and the attenuating effect of sulfate aerosols would be diminished. Considering the environmental effects of acid rain, there is no reason to permit this process to continue.

Our discussion has dealt with wet precipitation but there is another way that SO_2 is removed from the atmosphere. About 25% of the removal of SO_2 from the air is by reaction of the gas with a surface film of water on vegetation and with sea spray. This reaction on vegetation surfaces involves hydrogen peroxide, as in the case of cloud droplets, and acts to acidify a surface film on vegetation. This so-called "dry deposition" (because it does not come down with rain or snow) of sulfur can directly influence the chemistry of vegetation. The removal of needed elements like potassium and sodium from the plant surface by leaching under acid conditions might affect growth and diminish the defenses of plants.

The other source of acid rain is nitric oxide gases designated as NO_x. These gases are produced at present primarily by the high-temperature combustion of fossil fuels. But in this case not only are power plants implicated but also cars and trucks. The nitrogen comes from the air itself that is drawn in to burn the fuel. The high temperature of the flame causes the combustion of nitrogen and oxygen to form gaseous NO_x.

Like sulfur dioxide conversion to sulfuric acid, gaseous NO_x also must be oxidized to form nitric acid. The production of NO_x is areally broader than it is for sulfur dioxide because of the addition of the internal combustion engine source to the power plant source. Another source of NO_x is soils treated with nonorganic fertilizers. This source, however, is considerably smaller than the combustion sources.

The changes in the amount of sulfuric and nitric acid delivery over time are shown in Figure 9–2. Clearly, anthropogenic sulfate deposition is on the wane, but nitrate deposition is increasing. We have been controlling emissions of SO_2 from coal-fired power plants but we are only now developing methods of controlling NO_x emissions. Sulfuric acid and nitric acid are the major components of acid precipitation. The production of acid in soils by the formation of weak acids like oxalic acid and citric acid and the production of carbonic acid by the oxidation of organic matter are more important than these human-accelerated acid sources in the weathering of Earth's surface. The importance

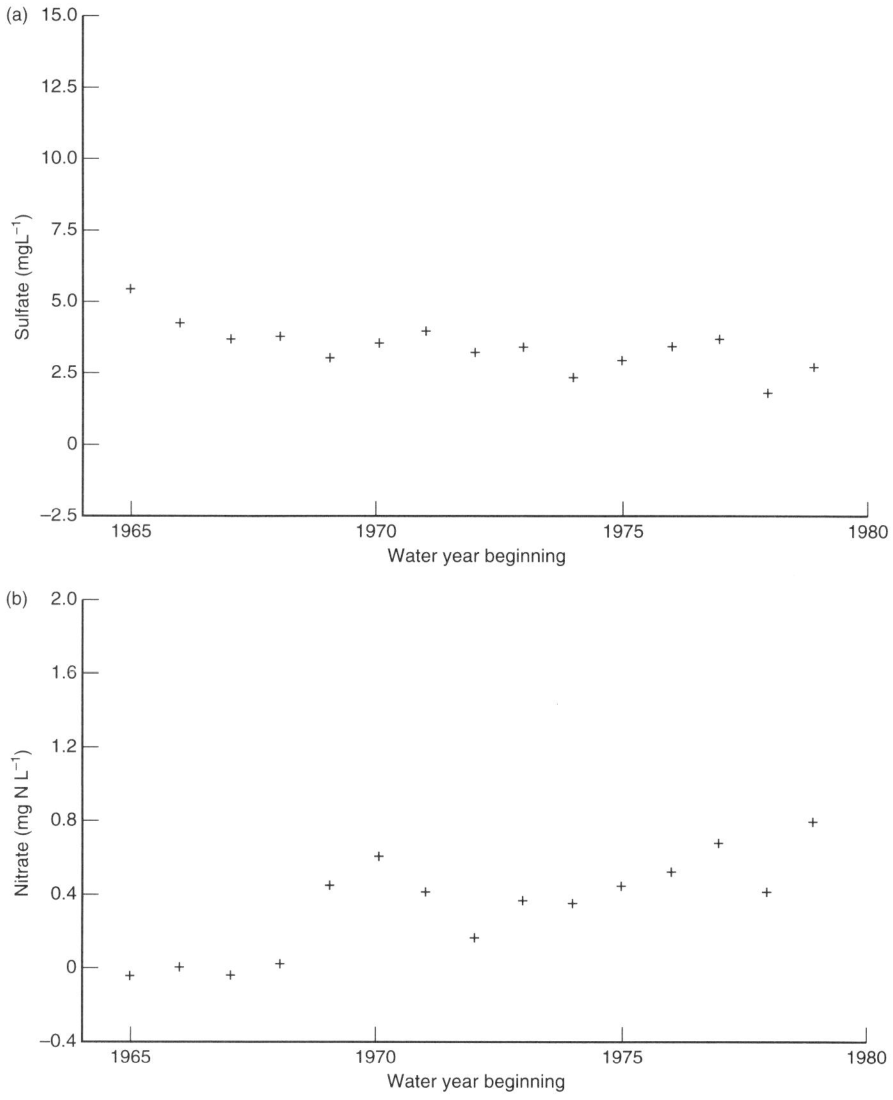

FIGURE 9–2 Changes in precipitation chemistry at the Hinckley, New York, USGS site. (a) Sulfate concentration, and (b) nitrate concentration. Data are from monthly bulk-deposition samples. (Summary from National Research Council Report, *Acid Deposition*, 1986, National Academy Press.)

of human-accelerated acid production is that the produced hydrogen ions directly interact with whatever is exposed to its assault from the air—by wet precipitation or interactions of the gases on surfaces. Limestone buildings and marble statues are obvious victims of acid precipitation, but so are all other surfaces subject to corrosion by acid. The effect of increased hydrogen ion fluxes on unbuffered lakes, such as many in the Adirondacks, has been to dissolve clay minerals and burden the water with biologically toxic chemicals (when present in high concentration) such as aluminum. The effect on vegetation can also be considerable, but the broad regional effects on large forests such as the Black Forest of Germany or the Blue Ridge Mountains in the eastern United States may be due to increased ozone production in the troposphere by human actions. The role of acid rain on the major weathering cycle locally is trivial compared to the aggressive production of organic acids, and ultimately carbonic acid, by the natural activity of living organisms.

TROPOSPHERIC OZONE

In the previous chapter the discussion of stratospheric ozone production and destruction was the major concern because of the molecule's capacity to block biologically harmful ultraviolet radiation. In the troposphere, ozone is also produced but its effects there are generally considered harmful, acting as an oxidant. The small amount of natural ozone that is produced in the troposphere has been augmented by human activities. The vision of a city shrouded in smog is one of the strongest reminders of the environmental impacts of anthropogenic emissions of reactive gases. It is the presence of ozone (O_3) in these regions that causes the greatest concern because of the harmful effects on humans, especially those with respiratory problems, and on vegetation. The record of increase in tropospheric ozone is not available from ice cores or other archival data because ozone is quickly destroyed. A record of ozone changes from the nineteenth century in Europe has been identified (Fig. 9–3).

Ozone, unlike SO_2 and NO_x, is not a direct gaseous emission but is the product of reactions of other gases injected into the atmosphere from ground level under the influence of sunlight (Fig. 9–4). These sunlight-activated reactive gases are the oxides of nitrogen and volatile organic compounds (VOCs). The volatile organic compounds come from a number of sources both anthropogenic and naturally biotic. The anthropogenic sources are generally associated with petroleum and petrochemicals. The smells of gasoline, unspent products of ignition, and chemicals used as solvents or starting materials in manufacturing are common experiences you may have with anthropogenic volatile organic compounds. In addition to these odoriferous, volatile, organic compounds, others without strong smells are also injected into the atmosphere by human activities. Vegetation also releases volatile organic compounds to the air. The smells of pine trees and the fragrances of flowers and bushes all attest to the natural release of volatile organic compounds to the air. Indeed

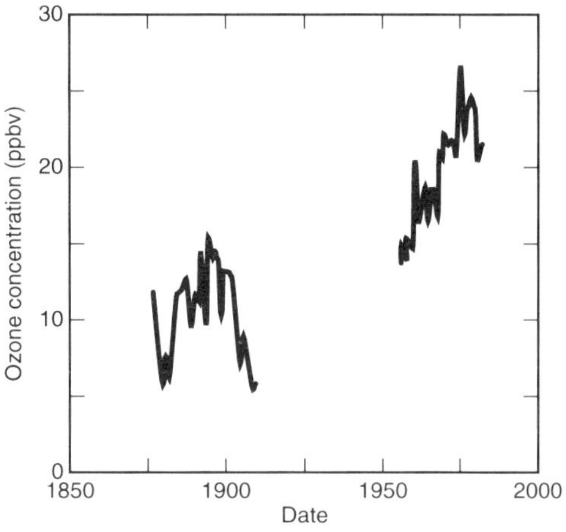

FIGURE 9–3 A comparison of 1876–1907 surface ozone volume mixing ratios at Montsouris (near Paris) with those in 1956–1982 at Arkona, Germany. (A. Volz and D. Kley, *Nature,* v. 332, p. 240. Reprinted with permission, copyright Macmillan Magazines Limited.)

the contribution of vegetatively derived VOC to the atmosphere in some areas, including cities, may equal or exceed the anthropogenic loading.

Through a complex set of molecular reactions involving VOCs and NO_x in the presence of sunlight, ozone is created (see Appendix 9–1). As ozone is formed only in sunlight, the amount generated in the troposphere during the day decreases at night as the result of oxidative reactions that are not light dependent. These reactions occur with the ground surface as well as in the atmosphere. Figure 9–5 summarizes the reaction pathways.

Some surprising results emerge from analyzing the VOC–NO_x reaction. For example, for low concentrations of NO_x there is no increase in the amount of ozone no matter how much the concentration of VOC increases. The biggest effect is to increase NO_x at the same time that VOC is increased. Another paradoxical situation arises when, at relatively low levels of VOC, efforts are made to decrease only NO_x. In that case the ozone concentration in the air actually *increases* with decreasing NO_x. The air from a highly polluted central city area moving toward the less settled regions may actually decrease in NO_x due to deposition, as described in the discussion of acid precipitation. If VOC does not change markedly, the situation of increasing ozone in the air in the periphery of cities will occur.

Although decreasing anthropogenic VOC generally will lower ozone, the ubiquitous biotic VOC can set a higher level of ozone than if NO_x emissions are not controlled. For example, if anthropogenic VOC were diminished but biotic VOC remained high, the limiting conditions for the production of ozone would be the NO_x level. A very high NO_x level maintained from intense point (for example, a city or a power plant) or pervasive (cars, trucks) sources, when reaching a remote forest could, by reactions with

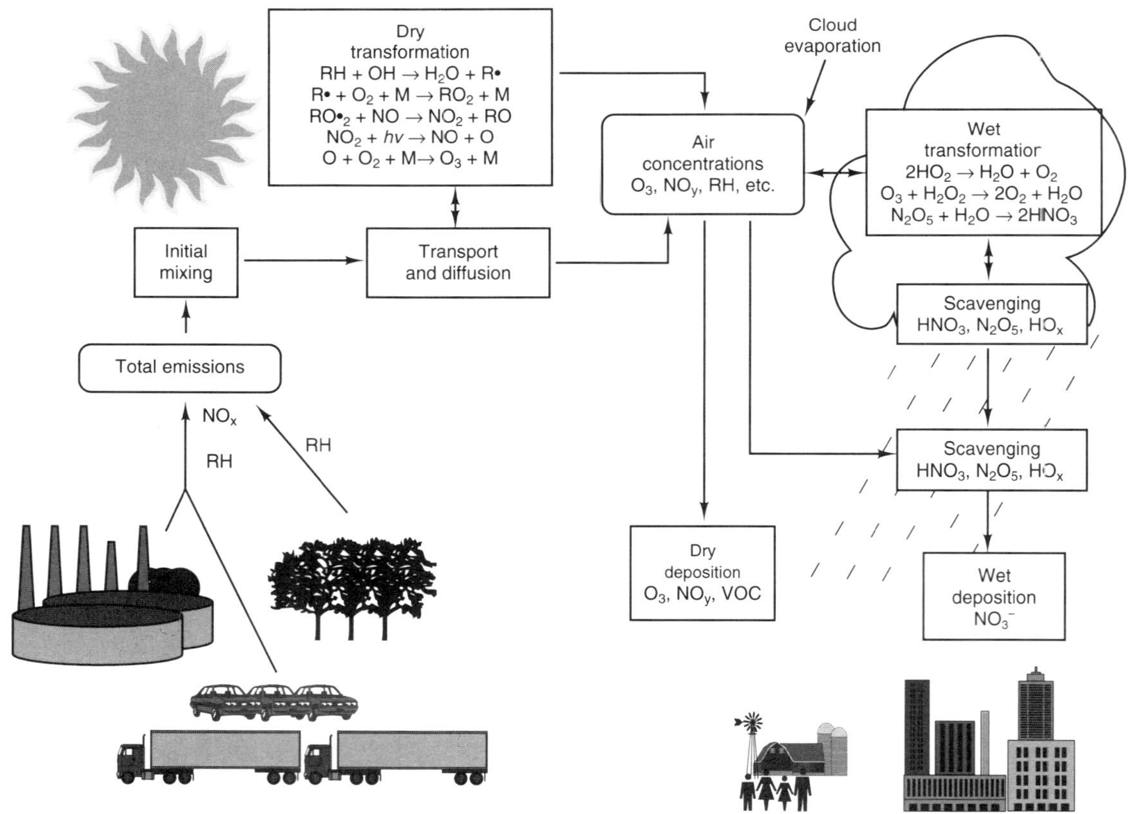

FIGURE 9–4 Photochemical air pollution, from emission to deposition. See Appendix 9–1 for discussion of reactions. NO_y includes volatile HNO_3, as well as NO and NO_2. (From National Research Council Report, *Rethinking the Ozone Problem in Urban and Regional Air Pollution*, 1991, National Academy Press.)

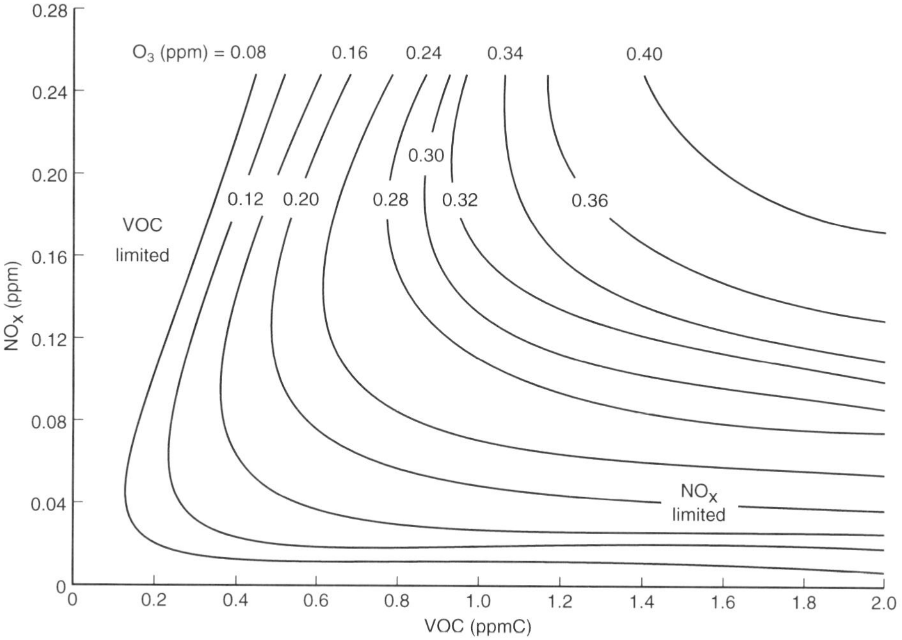

FIGURE 9–5 Relationship between NO_x and VOC concentrations in air and the resulting concentrations of ozone produced by their reaction, based on empirical kinetic modeling approach by the U.S. Environmental Protection Agency. (From National Research Council Report, *Rethinking the ozone problem in urban and regional pollution*, 1991, National Academy Press.)

the locally produced biotic VOC, create ozone at sufficiently high levels to endanger the forest's health.

The regulation of both NO_x and VOC emissions must take into consideration not only the complexities of photochemical reactions but also the highly transient meteorological factors that can move both ozone and its precursor reactants away from highly polluted regions. Regulation of NO_x and VOC emissions must follow the controls imposed by these two complex physical effects.

The relationship of the tropospheric ozone increase to global environmental change is a subtle one. As more and more people move to the cities and the NO_x concentration increases, the radial transfer of NO_x away from the city may actually impact rural areas with high enough VOC to trigger ozone production far from cities. As the most destructive of the atmospherically produced chemical species (so far as plants are concerned) is coupled directly to ozone concentrations, the transfer of city-based pollution to the

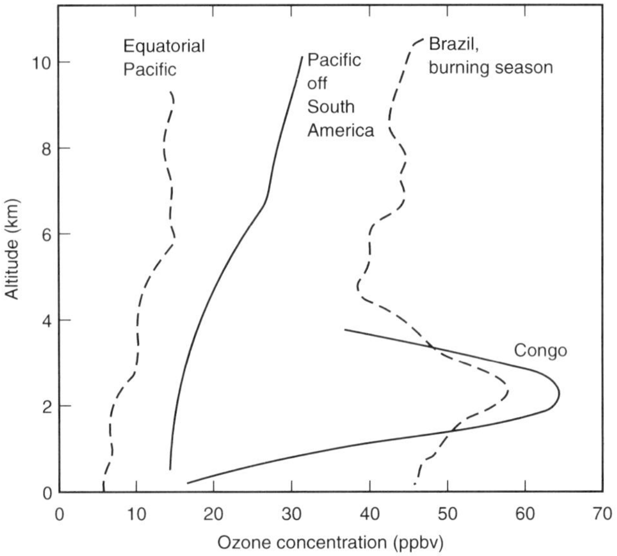

FIGURE 9–6 Ozone concentration vertical profiles in the tropical troposphere. The ozone profiles over Brazil and the Congo region of Zaire show high ozone concentrations between 1 and 4 kilometers altitude due to photochemical production in biomass-burning plumes. The profile over the equatorial Pacific shows no influence from biomass-burning. The profile over the Pacific off South America suggests ozone transport from Brazil. (Reprinted with permission from P. J. Crutzen and M. O. Andreae, 1990, *Science,* v. 250, p. 1669. Copyright American Association for the Advancement of Science.)

surrounding rural lands can cause serious changes in the health of forests and farm crops. The extensive damage to forests, if sustained, can have feedback effects on water retention and other environmental parameters. It is these secondary effects that make the production of tropospheric ozone a global and not just a local problem.

In addition to the formation of ozone in cities, a major source comes from massive biomass burning as occurs virtually continuously in the low latitudes of Africa and South America. Indeed the levels of ozone in these areas can far exceed the amounts found around cities (Fig. 9–6).

PROBLEM:

A. If acid rain has a pH of 4 and precipitation in a region is 100 cm, how much H^+ (in moles) is delivered per cm^2 to the soil in one year by the precipitation of acid rain?

B. If half of the removal of SO_2 and NO_x is by gas reactions with water layers on vegetation ("dry deposition"), how much additional H^+ per cm^2 can be available to the soil surface in a year?

C. How many grams of calcium carbonate must be added per year per cm^2 to soil to neutralize the acid from both wet and dry deposition?

D. The decay of vegetative material produces carbon dioxide. Half of this carbon dioxide is released to the atmosphere directly. The other half dissolves in percolating groundwater to form carbonic acid (H_2CO_3). How much H^+ (in moles per cm^2 per year) is produced if H_2CO_3 completely dissociates and the annual carbon fixing rate is 1.1×10^{17} grams of carbon per year?

E. If half the precipitation is lost by transpiration and evaporation and the other half percolates downward in the soil, what is the pH of the water if the carbonic acid completely dissociates and no other reactions occur?

APPENDIX 9–1: MAINTAINING A HIGH LEVEL OF OZONE IN THE TROPOSPHERE

The reactions are generalized as follows:

$$RH + OH \rightarrow R + H_2O$$

where RH represents a generalized volatile organic compound with one reactive hydrogen bond identified, and OH is the oxidant, the hydroxyl radical, and R is the resulting reactive organic radical (having lost the hydrogen). The next reaction is

$$R + O_2 + M \rightarrow RO_2 + M$$

where M is an inert third molecule needed to take off the excess energy of reaction to promote the formation of reactive RO_2. Finally, the role of NO comes into play:

$$RO_2 + NO \rightarrow NO_2 + RO$$

NO_2 is further photodissociated so that

$$NO_2 + h\nu \rightarrow NO + O$$

and NO again enters into the cycle of reactions given above. The final reaction producing ozone is

$$O + O_2 + M \rightarrow O_3 + M$$

Ozone is dissociated by ultraviolet light so that

$$O_3 + h\nu \rightarrow O_2 + O$$

The activated O then reacts with water to produce OH and the cycle begins again. By this process a high level of ozone can be maintained in the troposphere.

10

HUMAN MIGRATION, POPULATION GROWTH, AND ENVIRONMENTAL CHANGE

Aside from the smog of cities, most of the changes in atmospheric chemistry are not directly observable without proper instrumentation. The environmental effects of these changes are inferred from laboratory and theoretical studies. This situation is not the case, however, for changes that have been occurring in land and water use. These changes are the inevitable consequences of human population growth and consequent exploitation of the terrain for sustenance. We are more formidable in our modification of the terrain than beavers who build dams, sheep and goats who graze to the point of the transformation of grassed areas to dustbowls, or even elephants turning forests into the appearance of a battlefield as the result of their browsing. We have transformed forests to farmlands, built aggressively on wetlands, and altered natural waterways to such an extent that these various changes can be seen both from the land and also from satellites.

Natural changes have determined the history of the human race. Humans, as their numbers have increased on Earth, have changed the environment and influenced the natural history of life on the planet.

THE ORIGINS OF FARMING AND WESTERN CIVILIZATION

In Chapter 5 the changes in the intensity of the monsoons affecting the Indian subcontinent, western Asia, and northern Africa were related to the 20,000-year precession cycle. About 10,000 years ago the monsoons were more intense than at the present time because Earth was closer to the sun in northern summer than it is now. At that time the Sahara Desert and the comparable areas in Asia, all affected by the increased monsoonal intensity, were vast green terrains rather than the deserts they are today. How did the change affect the behavior of humans?

About 10,000 years ago human tribal groups wandered across the large, well-watered fields and forests of the Sahara, southwest Asia, and southern Asia hunting and gathering. Archaeological remains show campsites along old river channels and bones of the animals that were hunted. As the climate deteriorated and the monsoons weakened, desertification set in and the animals and their pursuers, humans, retreated bit by bit to river valleys where the perennial supply of water from the remote mountains allowed the maintenance of life, although under highly competitive conditions. The population, which was originally spread out over large tracts of land, was focused virtually along a line, and the need for social structure and a dependable food supply was required for survival. Luckily, agriculture had been developed, prior to this crisis in the environment, by local tribes living in the mountains of the Middle East. The safety of remote valleys watered by orogenic precipitation allowed for a self-sufficient existence based on agriculture. Their small-plot farming and animal husbandry were welcome technologies for the people crowding along the river banks. Once this technology was transferred to the people along the large rivers in the plains, the great valley civilizations of Egypt, Mesopotamia, and India were established. These civilizations dominated the land around them because of their large, concentrated populations and tightly structured societies.

Farming spread from the Near East to the northwest tip of Europe in about 4000 years starting about 9000 years ago (as we are dating back from the present, we call the date of this spreading 9000 years B.P.—"before present") carried by people from the southeast knowledgeable in farming practices, who encountered and intermarried with people in the north (Fig. 10–1). The northernmost inhabitants were new arrivals from Asia following the retreating ice of the last great ice advance. Many had developed a lifestyle that depended on the sea for transport and nourishment. The change to an agrarian-based lifestyle can be seen in the analysis of the remains of ancient Norsemen compared to living Scandinavians.

The record of diet change is in the form of the isotopic composition of carbon and nitrogen in the organic matter found in bones. Carbon compounds in ancient bones (collagen) of Norsemen recovered from graves over 5000 years old showed that they dined almost exclusively on marine food, much as the modern Greenlanders do. From 5000 B.P. to the present, Scandinavians have, like most Europeans, bone organic matter with a carbon

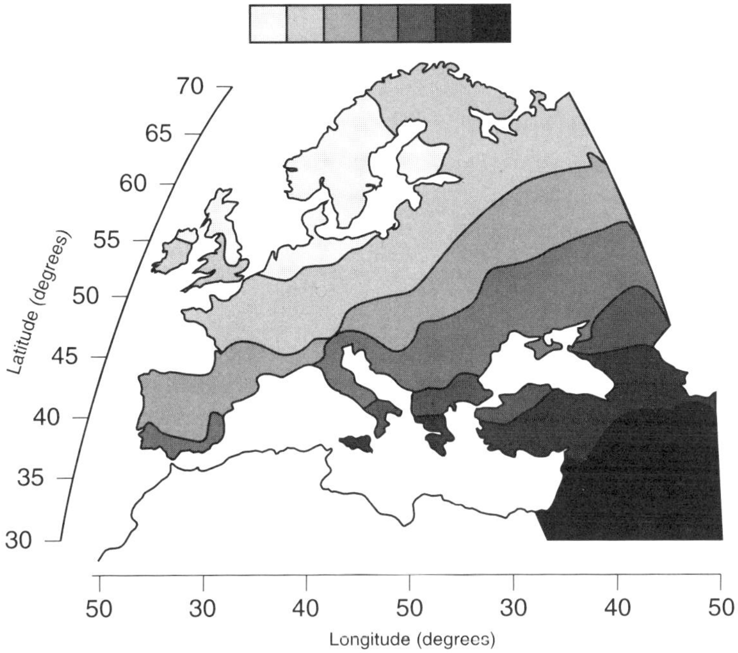

FIGURE 10–1 The gradient of genetic characteristics from southeastern Europe to northwestern Europe (shading is based on arbitrary scale). The pattern resembles the pattern of first introduction of agriculture as determined by radiocarbon dating. The introduction of agriculture was effected by migration and intermarriage. The rate was about one kilometer a year. (Reprinted with permission from L. L. Cavalli-Sforza, P. Menozi and A. Piazza, 1993, *Science,* v. 259, p. 639. Copyright American Association for the Advancement of Science.)

isotope signature indicating an agrarian diet. It is this change-over that gave the clue to the time of the arrival of agriculture to the northwestern part of Europe (Fig. 10–2).

This abbreviated summary is presented to show that humans have adapted in complex technological and social ways as dramatic changes took place around them as the result of irresistible natural forces. Humans have always adjusted to these changes, although the ensuing structure of society and the freedom of humans has not always been the ideal we imagine based on our contemporary sense of liberty and justice.

HUMAN MIGRATIONS AND THE SETTLEMENT OF THE CONTINENTS

The genetic relationships among the humans of the world show that patterns of migrations are not restricted to one continent but can cross oceans. As the

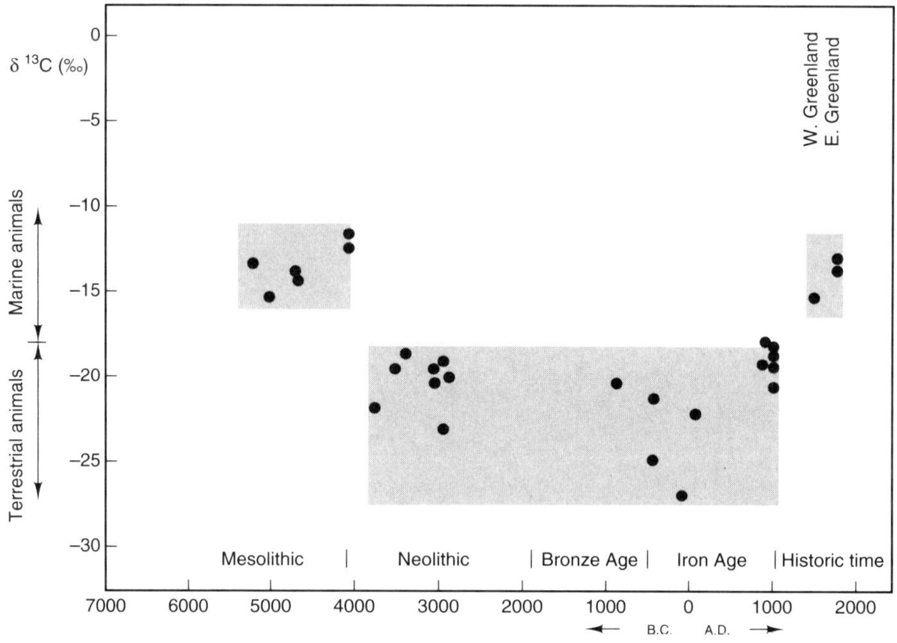

FIGURE 10–2 The change in $\delta^{13}C$ in remains of ancient Norse populations showing the transformation in diet from mainly marine foods to agricultural products. (After H. Tauber, 1981, *Nature,* v. 292, p. 332. Reprinted with permission, copyright Macmillan Magazines Limited.)

human species spread across the world, genetic variations occurred, in part due to adaptations to the various environments they encountered. Although *Homo erectus* and *Homo sapiens neanderthalensis* as well as *Homo sapiens sapiens* (modern humans) remains are found throughout Africa and Eurasia, only *Homo sapiens sapiens* remains are found in the western hemisphere and Australia. Based on the dating of remains, the populating of these two parts of the world occurred less than 50,000 years ago, sometime during the last major glacial cycle.

At one time it was thought that the lowering of sea level during times of extensive continental glaciation provided land bridges between continents over which human migration could occur. A case for this viewpoint could be made based on the fact that there would be emergence of the land now covered by the Bering Sea should sea level drop. The land between Siberia and Alaska so formed was called Beringia. We now know that migrations from Siberia to Alaska and further down the North American coast could be the consequence of transportation by sea. The quest for marine food could result in island hopping across the Aleutians no matter what the sea level was. If the ancestors of the native Americans derived their food primarily from the sea, then travel by boat or raft was the likely agent of colonization of North America.

Marine travel was required for the settlement of Australia. Remains of Australian aborigine settlements are as old as 32,000 years B.P. and there are suggestions that the actual initial settlement of Australia occurred as far back as 50,000 years B.P. Based on bathymetric maps of the seas around Indonesia, New Guinea, and Australia, it is obvious that no matter how much lower sea level was during glacial times, the deep trench between New Guinea and Indonesia would never be exposed. Humans could only get to New Guinea and Australia by boats or rafts.

We conclude that the environment has provided the need for humans to use resourceful means to populate Earth. The migrations of humans were driven by the quest for food and by curiosity, the hallmark of our species. The limiting control on the survival of humans was the availability of fresh water responsible for the growth of vegetation and the support of fauna. The excursions at sea were a link along this search. The entire world was to feel the environmental impact of human migrations.

THE NEW WORLD: THE IMPACT OF SETTLEMENT ON THE ENVIRONMENT

When humans first arrived in the Americas over 10,000 years ago they found a land rich in fauna, including pachyderms (mastodons and wooly mammoths), horses, bison, and creatures related to the Old World camels (for example, llamas). The pachyderms and horses became extinct prior to or soon after humans arrived. Of the large animals, only the bison remained in North America and the camel-like creatures remained in South America. The coincidence of the arrival of humans and the extinction of species may not be unrelated, although direct evidence may not be found (i.e., "the smoking gun"). The arrival of Europeans, in fairly recent times (since 1492 A.D.), with their vigorous hunting of the bison almost obliterated that species.

The obliteration of species by the arrival of humans is documented for smaller island systems and serves as a model of human impacts on the fauna of a region. For example, humans arrived on the Spanish island of Majorca in the Mediterranean about 3500 years B.P. The arrival of humans rang the death knell for the indigenous goat-like creature of that island (*Myotragus* sp.). This animal, unlike the goat, had binocular vision. This permitted good surveillance of the rocky terrain but was less advantageous for scanning for predators. The bone structure of fossil assemblages appears to show that these animals commonly reached old age, unlike animals subject to predators. This combination of fossil evidence implies an absence of predators on the island capable of threatening the animal—that is, until humans arrived. Soon after the arrival of humans, based on archaeological evidence, the goat-like species was obliterated from Earth.

A similar drive to extinction took place in the seventeenth century on the island of Mauritius in the Indian Ocean. The elegant dodo bird, a nonflying species indigenous to Mauritius, was hunted down and killed. The awareness of the effects of humans on the survival of species, exemplified by the extinction of the dodo bird, was responsible for the start of a conservation movement among Europeans. Although not wholly successful even now, the conservation program did come in the nick of time, as virtually every corner of the world was visited by Europeans by the end of the eighteenth century, with the increased chance of driving newly encountered species into extinction.

In the New World the effects of humans eventually went beyond the putative decimation of the fauna. About 4000 years ago an agricultural crop, maize, was developed, which would have far-reaching consequences. Maize belongs to a group of plants that includes sugar cane, sorghum, crabgrass, and much of the native grasses of the Great Plains (see Appendix 7–2). This group of plants photosynthesizes by a different pathway than the way the rest of the common plants, such as wheat, rice, trees, and bushes, do. The first group is designated C_4, the latter C_3 (indicating the photosynthetic pathways). The C_4 plants are characterized by thriving in low-carbon dioxide, low-water, and high-temperature environments. The origins of maize agriculture began in Mesoamerica where the conditions ideal for C_4 plants exist. As maize cultivation dominated the food supply of the growing settled population, major changes took place in the land. The increased agriculture depleted the forests that remained and increased soil erosion.

The arrival of the Spaniards after Columbus's voyage in 1492 A.D. may have had some effects on the environment, especially in the scarring and polluting of the land by mining, but the effect of agriculture was very much an indigenous process. Studies of lake deposits in Mexico document the changes in the amount of erosion due to the conversion of forested land to maize cultivation. These dated deposits give evidence of the aggressive farming that was in place even before Europeans arrived and introduced the plow (Fig. 10–3).

The spread of maize throughout western North America was accomplished by 1000 A.D. The arrival of maize cultivation east of the Mississippi River occurred about 1000 years ago. The basis of this knowledge is in the study of carbon isotopes in plants and bones (Fig. 10–4). C_4 plants are more enriched in the heavy stable isotope of carbon (^{13}C) than C_3 plants, and this difference is maintained in bone collagen even in fossil bones. Maize was probably introduced by migration of some of the southwestern peoples traveling up

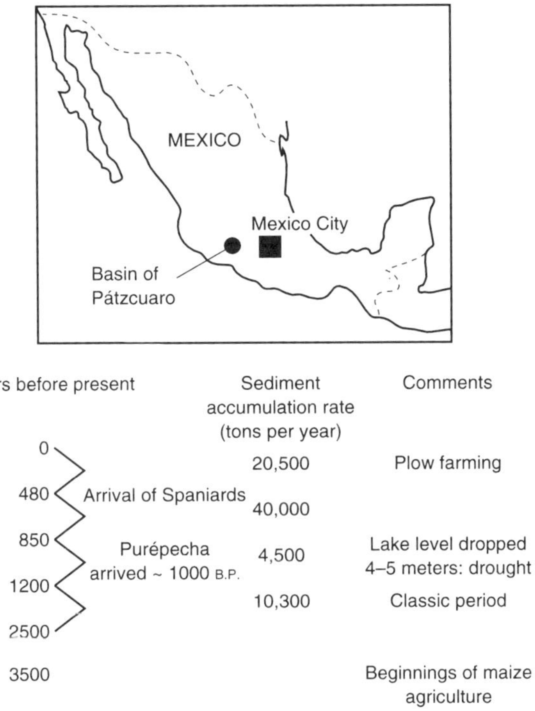

FIGURE 10–3 The erosional effects of farming in Mesoamerica. Sediment accumulation in Lake Pátzcuaro (Mexico) changes due to human activity. (After S. L. O'Hara, F. A. Street-Perrott, and T. P. Burt, 1993, *Nature,* v. 362, p. 48.)

the Mississippi River. Almost instantaneously the idea of maize agriculture spread all the way to the east coast of North America. The land was suited to the exploitation of maize since the climatic conditions of the midwest and northeast allowed maize to grow especially well. The small plants of the semi-arid environments of Mesoamerica became the large, productive plants of the northeast because of higher rainfall in the northeast compared to the southwest. The changes in the land resulting from maize agriculture in pre-European North America are well documented.

The arrival of Europeans and the transfer of maize cultivation to the new settlers ultimately led to the vast agricultural empires of North America. Striking changes in the environment took place. The midwestern states, Iowa and Illinois for example, in their pre-European state could be classified as "wetlands." It was the draining of these wetlands that permitted the development of extensive agriculture, which now makes the United States an important food resource for the whole world.

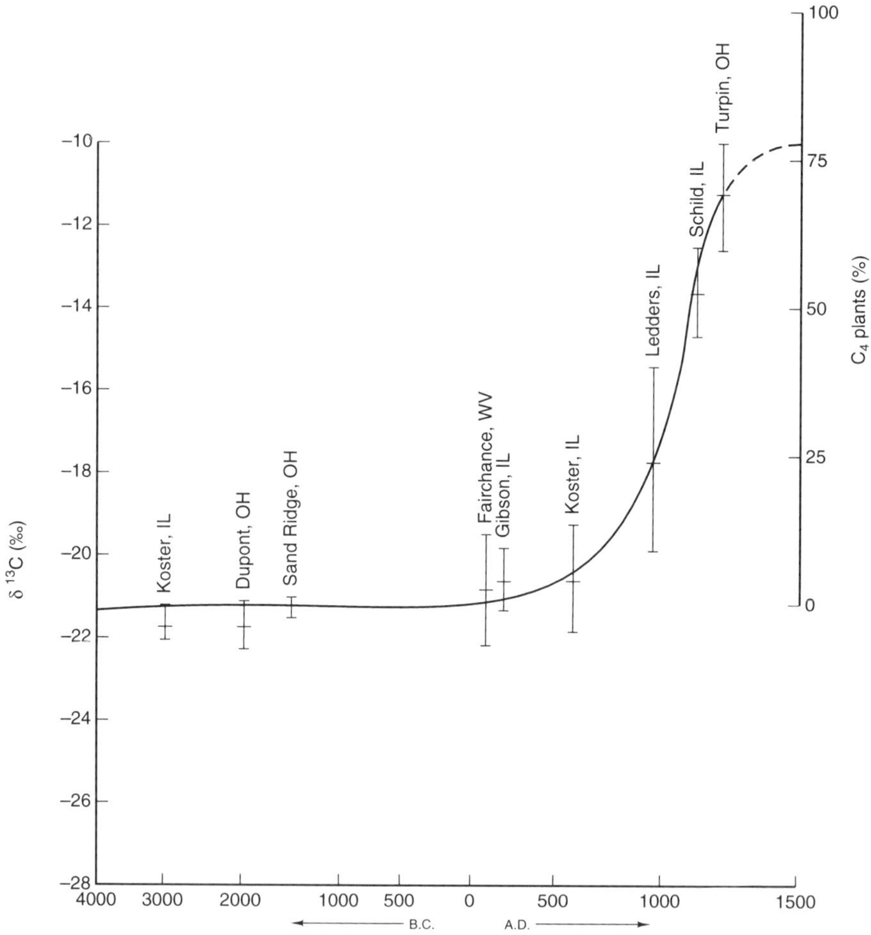

FIGURE 10–4 Introduction of maize agriculture to northeastern North America as seen in the carbon isotope shift in bone collagen of ancient humans. (After N. J. van der Merwe and J. C. Vogel, 1976, *Nature,* v. 276, p. 815.)

Another wetland was obliterated as the result of the success of midwestern agriculture and western livestock management. The construction of Chicago is a massive transformation of a wetland into a population center. The encroachment of humans on wetlands has proceeded all over the world, but perhaps geographically most extensively in the United States.

In summary, the quest for a stable food supply led to the development of a vast maize-based agriculture throughout the New World. The increased erosion and alteration of the land followed. The spread of maize agriculture to northeastern North America 1000 years ago poised the continent for massive agricultural exploitation once Europeans arrived and spread westward in the nineteenth century. No longer would the face of North America be the same as it was before the arrival of the first humans over ten thousand years ago.

WATER

The rivers of the world have been changed by the actions of humans. The decrease in monsoonal precipitation in south Asia and north Africa since about 9000 years ago, as discussed, and the increasing population of these areas have put a strong demand on the water supply and the dependent vegetation. The water of the Indus River with its tributaries no longer reaches the sea because it is being used for the needs of the people of Pakistan and India. Now that all the water of this once mighty stream has been consigned to irrigation, groundwater has begun to be pumped down to such an extent that its quality has deteriorated rapidly. A similar situation is developing along the Nile. The development of the Aswan dam for water control not only inundated vast archaeological sites but heralded the forthcoming water problems of Egypt's growing population. In the United States, the Colorado River is reduced to a trickle by the time it reaches the Gulf of California, as water is drawn off to supply the needs of the growing population of the southwestern states.

A major example of river control with consequences far beyond its intention is found in the management of the Ganges River in India. Arising in the Himalayas, it traverses northeastern India and debouches into the Bay of Bengal through an extensive deltaic terrain that constitutes the country of Bangladesh. The Ganges has been dammed along its course and levees have been built to channel the water so that the runoff from the strong monsoonal rains of the summer can be controlled in a region of farming important to the Indian economy. One result of this control of the Ganges is that 30% more water is transported along the channel than before leveeing. This excess water is delivered to Bangladesh during the summer monsoons. The dams, at least until they are silted up, inhibit the transfer of detritus to the delta. The increased supply of water and the decreased supply of silt act together to make Bangladesh vulnerable to storms and raging coastal seas.

Even if the Ganges water problem in Bangladesh could be solved by the construction of diversionary channels directly to the ocean, the storms would still be of concern. This problem will always be serious with the population density of Bangladesh. The almost 100,000 deaths a year due to storms, erosion, and flooding are more than compensated for by the reproduction rate of the populace. The high competition for space in the region prevents the alleviation of the population growth by migration. The fierce, almost genocidal, wars of the region attest to that. The control for Bangladesh then appears to be population more than water or wind. Preparing for the possible future rise in sea level is secondary to the engineering control of the Ganges system and orders of magnitude less important than controlling population growth. Clearly issues of global change for Bangladesh are of minor importance compared to the issue of population control.

The other side of the water problem is its paucity in certain regions of the world. The desert regions become of concern either when the population encroaches on it, as in the southwestern United States, or if increased desertification occurs because of human activities. The most obvious example of the latter is the region at the southern margin of the Sahara Desert. As discussed earlier, the Sahara was a well-watered land about 9000 years ago as the result of more intense monsoonal circulation—the consequence of the precession cycle. As the Sahara has dried up over the years, the desert has expanded southward. The increase in population and the subsequent increased need for water and food gradually depleted these commodities in the region we call the Sahel—the fringe area between the desert and green Africa. The conspiracy of nature and humans has made this region of Africa a place of intense suffering. The change in the environment and the growth of population not only have increased child mortality but also have resulted in the fierce encounters of competing tribes for the diminishing resources.

In the United States, overfarming coupled with natural changes in climate resulted in the Dust Bowl of the midwest states in the early 1930s. The resulting erosion of the topsoil and the forced migration of impoverished farmers were poignantly related in the book *The Grapes of Wrath* by John Steinbeck. Such erosion of the landscape by wind and water has devastated China and other heavily populated countries. The loss of topsoil retards agricultural development and results in the movement of peoples. The human encounters resulting from such displacements add to the social woes of both the displaced and the neighbors into whose territory movement occurs.

Finally, the depletion of the water we obtain from the ground through springs and wells has reached noticeable proportions (see Table 6–1). The groundwater table has been lowered in many parts of the world, such as the Ogalala aquifer of the region from Nebraska to Texas. This aquifer supplies northwestern Texas with the irrigation water necessary for farming. The level of this vast underground water reservoir has dropped by about 55 feet in the last 50 years. Ancient groundwaters are being mined in now-desert regions of the world, from Saudi Arabia to Arizona. These water resources are not being replenished as fast as they are being used. Not only has the quantity of water stored underground diminished all around the world, the quality has also been changing. The conscious or unconscious dumping of toxic chemicals into aquifers has polluted water supplies.

11

NATURAL CATASTROPHES AND THE HISTORY OF LIFE

Our catalog of dire changes wrought by nature or humans includes a number of categories. These categories are accidents, disasters, or catastrophes, depending on the extent of the effect or its intensity. The Biblical Deluge, for example, in which the whole of Earth flooded and no one escaped except as the result of divinely inspired planning, has provided the measure of our concept of global "catastrophe." Indeed, the development of geologic thought in the early nineteenth century grew out of the debate about the credibility of a literal interpretation of such a catastrophic event.

Our contemporary vision of catastrophe is provided by the prospect of all-out nuclear war. The argument has been made that not only would massive immediate human deaths result from a nuclear holocaust, but there would be a radical change in the environment that would affect all life. This predicted radical change would not be caused by pervasive radiation effects, but rather by the strong atmospheric effects resulting from the massive bombing of cities. The sun's rays would be blocked from Earth's surface for several months due to the conflagrations resulting from the bombing of the substance of civilization—plastics and oil storage facilities and refineries. This catastrophic scenario has been called "nuclear winter."

Has Earth ever experienced natural catastrophes of large magnitudes and can we expect human-induced catastrophes resulting from our subtle tampering with the environment? We have some indication of the former and this knowledge may help us evaluate the latter.

EPISODIC CHANGES IN THE GEOLOGIC RECORD

The debate about the history of life on Earth started long before Charles Darwin published his classic theory of evolution in 1859. At the end of the eighteenth century and into the early part of the nineteenth century a debate between two schools of geologic thought took place. One group, dubbed with the sobriquet Neptunists, thought that all rocks at the planet's surface were due to deposition from a global ocean, commonly, but not necessarily, identified as the Noahic Flood of the Bible. Even rocks that we now recognize as intrusive layers of once-molten magma forced between layers of pre-existing sediments were thought to have been deposited serially, over a short span of time, from a global ocean. The Vulcanists thought that active volcanism existed throughout Earth's history (however long that was) and the rock record was a combination of material deposited from fluid water and air and hot volcanic material from Earth's interior.

The latter argument won the day by the evidence provided by a Scottish physician-farmer-geologist named James Hutton who, in 1795, enunciated the geologic axiom we call the principle of uniformity. That is, the geologic record could be explained by processes we see acting in the present. Volcanic eruptions, deltaic deposition, distortions of the surface expressed as mountains, and the many other processes observable by investigating the world today could also be seen to have occurred in the past by a careful study of the record in the rocks. Hutton argued that long periods of time were required to explain the geologic features of Earth and he went so far as to state that he "saw no vestige of a beginning and no prospect of an end." This practical viewpoint provided a way to understand the message left in rocks and was responsible for much of the successful interpretation of the geologic record to which we turn in understanding the history of Earth.

The uniformitarian view was espoused by many geologists of the early nineteenth century. The influential book of that time was written by Charles Lyell and called *Principles of Geology.* This book went through several editions and influenced a generation of scientists. Having read Charles Lyell's book during his training as a natural scientist, Charles Darwin was a product of this uniformitarian point of view. Darwin's theory of evolution was founded on the idea of natural selection. The fittest survived and reproduced their own kind when subject to competition with members of their own species and other species or in escaping predation by other species. The role of the changing environmental setting provided the framework in which this competition occurred. Although the records of both environmental and species changes were preserved in rocks, Darwin never felt comfortable in using the paleontologic evidence to certify his evolutionary theory in writing.

His hesitation lay in the fact that the record of life in sedimentary rocks did not show a clear drift of species. Rather, there seemed to be sharp changes which seemed to have a catastrophic quality, even though some of this could be attributed to the incompleteness of the record.

The sharp changes in assemblages of species were recognized in 1812 by the French scientist Georges Cuvier, a renowned anatomist and a careful paleontologist. Cuvier studied the sedimentary rocks of the region around Paris. These were relatively soft rocks that we now know to have formed about 100 million years ago. He found sharp changes in the species assemblages as he ascended the stratigraphic column. The lower strata were deposited before the higher strata in the geologic section even if the section was tilted because of later tectonic movements after initial deposition (this is called the principle of superposition). He ascribed these changes to a series of gigantic catastrophes, the last of which he equated with the Noahic Flood. Most living creatures were virtually destroyed at each catastrophe and were replaced by a few survivors and a new assemblage of living forms. This "catastrophism" represented global changes influencing the history of life. As most geologists had begun to embrace the uniformitarian view, few would accept the catastrophe interpretation invoked by Cuvier, and his views were dismissed as archaic if not actually in error.

Yet as paleontologists continued to study geologic strata, it became obvious that there were marked changes in life at critical times in the past. The geologic time chart discussed in Chapter 2 in large part was based on these paleontological studies. The boundaries between the Paleozoic, Mesozoic, and Cenozoic Eras are marked by sharp changes in the dominant species. Major extinctions and innovations of species on land and in the sea occurred over a short span of time at these boundaries. In addition to the major changes in life at the major boundaries demarking the three eras, smaller changes occurred throughout the Phanerozoic Eon and are the basis for delineating the periods discussed in Chapter 2. Clearly the major and minor changes confirmed, on a vast scale, the observations of Cuvier for a short time scale and a local region. Could these large changes be ascribed to catastrophes? If catastrophes occurred, what was their nature and how did they operate to eliminate whole species and not just individuals or restricted populations? Our answers come from a variety of apparently unlikely natural events.

Environmental causes resulting in catastrophic changes affecting life are fundamentally of three types. Continental glaciation in the northern hemisphere commencing 2.5 million years ago was accompanied by large swings in global temperature. The advance and retreat of ice in North America was parallel to the north-south mountain ranges so that migration of plants and animals was possible (Fig. 1–4). In Europe and Asia the mountain ranges run east to west so that the advancing ice sheets provided constricted passages for temperature-sensitive organisms (Fig. 1–4). For this reason there is a marked difference in the diversity of plants in the two hemispheres. These climate-geography changes, however, did not have global consequences.

Volcanic eruptions strongly attenuate the sun's radiation reaching Earth's surface by loading the stratosphere with tiny reflectors made of sulfuric acid droplets formed by the oxidation of the volcanic gases penetrating the tropopause. The strong cooling observed over Earth in recent times following such volcanic eruptions is a direct consequence of this attenuation of solar rays. If, in the past, large sustained volcanic eruptions occurred, then it is possible that sustained global cooling might have obtained and thereby affected the survival of some species worldwide. Such a possibility has been suggested for the major changes in species occurring at the end of the Eocene.

The role of impacting extraterrestrial bodies in influencing the evolution of Earth has been discussed in Chapter 1. The impact of a Mars-sized body with Earth early in the history of our planet is inferred to have created the moon and modified Earth's structure and atmosphere. Our study of cratering on other planetary bodies, as well as the events observed on Earth, indicate that collisions of asteroids and comets with our planet are not rare events. The severity of the effect of a collision depends on the size of the colliding body. Meteor Crater in Arizona (Fig. 11–1), for example, with a diameter of 1 km was made by an iron meteorite probably having a mass of 60,000 tons—about the mass of the battleship Missouri. The impact occurred about 100,000 years ago and there is no record of any biological changes that could be ascribed to this event. Clearly, to have a serious global effect the mass of the impacting body must be many times greater than the meteorite that formed Meteor Crater.

IMPACTS OF EXTRATERRESTRIAL OBJECTS WITH EARTH AND THE CRETACEOUS–TERTIARY (MESOZOIC–CENOZOIC) BOUNDARY

Perhaps the most spectacular of sharp transformations in the history of life occurred 65 million years ago. It was at this time that dinosaurs perished from Earth, and the small creatures scurrying around the feet of the dominant reptiles during the Mesozoic Era ultimately took over the planet.

The extinctions were more extensive than just involving the dinosaurs. Virtually every phylum in every habitat, land or sea, was decimated when the Cretaceous Period of the Mesozoic Era ended and the Tertiary of the Cenozoic Era began. The Cretaceous–Tertiary boundary rang the death knell for more

FIGURE 11–1 Meteor Crater in Arizona. The diameter of the crater is about 1 kilometer.

than 60% of the then extant species. The species that survived occupied special niches such as the ocean deeps, lakes, rivers (certain reptiles, such as turtles and crocodiles), and burrows (such as lizards and snakes and mammals).

The reasons for such a massive and extensive extinction of species have evaded paleontologists and biologists. A rampant viral or bacterial infection can be ruled out because of the vast variety of species and habitats that disappeared. The massive displacement of one species by others appears to be the consequence, not the agent, of the massive extinctions. For example, the small mammals that survived the end of the Cretaceous extinction event could not have caused the demise of the dinosaurs on land and sea and the variety of invertebrate marine faunas. Rather, the mammals became the inheritors of the terrains left vacated when the dinosaurs disappeared. The role played by organisms, either at the micro or macro level, in causing the extinction of the species at the Cretaceous–Tertiary boundary is not, therefore, a primary one. Rather we must look for a large-scale environmental cause capable of influencing creatures both on the land and in the oceans and virtually across the entire spectrum of life.

Of the three processes mentioned above, the extraterrestrial cause appears to be capable of the greatest extinction of species on a global level, if the impact were of large enough energy. It is the quest for understanding how such an impact could be identified and how it could have influenced the great transition occurring at the Cretaceous–Tertiary boundary that has involved scientists from a variety of disciplines. Not only must the presence of a large impact be attested to in the geologic record but the mechanism of species annihilation must be related to such an impact.

The evidence for a gigantic extraterrestrial impact comes from the analysis of sediment layers just at the Cretaceous–Tertiary boundary in both marine and continentally deposited strata. The characteristic imprint of a meteorite impact is the enrichment of elements diagnostic of extraterrestrial materials and the alteration in terrestrial minerals resulting from the powerful force accompanying a large collision. Iridium (Ir), a platinum group element, is present in high abundance in meteorites, in contrast to Earth's crustal rocks. The discovery of very high concentrations of iridium at the Cretaceous–Tertiary boundary clay layers everywhere convinced most people of the occurrence of an important cosmic impact event at that time. The unique cosmic origin of this layer has been confirmed by other chemical signatures characteristic of meteorites.

The resulting impact on Earth shocked the minerals in rocks much as strong nuclear test blasts do. Especially the common mineral quartz, a major constituent of most continental sands, shows patterns known to be producible only by impacts typical of meteorite impacts or nuclear explosions (Fig. 11–2). The ubiquitous presence of this shocked quartz at the Cretaceous–Tertiary boundary layer indicates without doubt that a meteorite was responsible for the event.

The location of "ground zero" of the impact is not known for sure but the best candidate appears to be the Yucatan peninsula in Mexico (Fig. 11–3). A large fossil meteorite crater found in the subsurface has the right size (about 120 km diameter) and is the right age to qualify as the large impact required at the Cretaceous–Tertiary boundary.

What could such a bombardment do to Earth's environment to result in such a massive extinction of species? There is no one answer to this question but several ideas have been proposed. The actual impact site would be locally destructive but in itself would not be detrimental to life on the planet as a whole. We must look to consequences that are global in impact. The most overwhelming effects are those involving changes in the atmosphere or

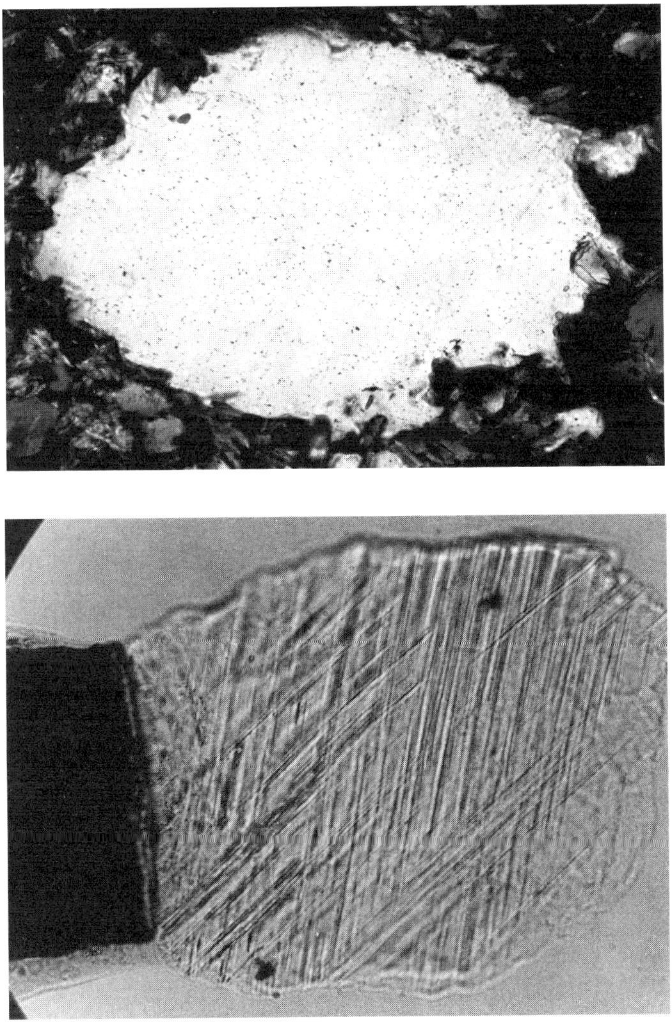

FIGURE 11–2 Lamellae in quartz are uniquely produced by high-energy explosions. The quartz grain in the top image (about 0.20 mm across) is one found in an ancient sedimentary rock and shows no features characteristic of shock due to explosion or impact. (Courtesy of Jay Ague, Yale University.) The quartz grain in the bottom image shows lamellae typical of explosion or impact. These shocked quartz grains have been found in sediments at the Cretaceous–Tertiary boundary throughout the world. This photomicrograph shows a grain of quartz (about 0.20 mm across) from the Cretaceous–Tertiary boundary in the Raton Basin near Trinidad, Colorado. (Courtesy of Glen A. Izett, U.S. Geological Survey, Emeritus.)

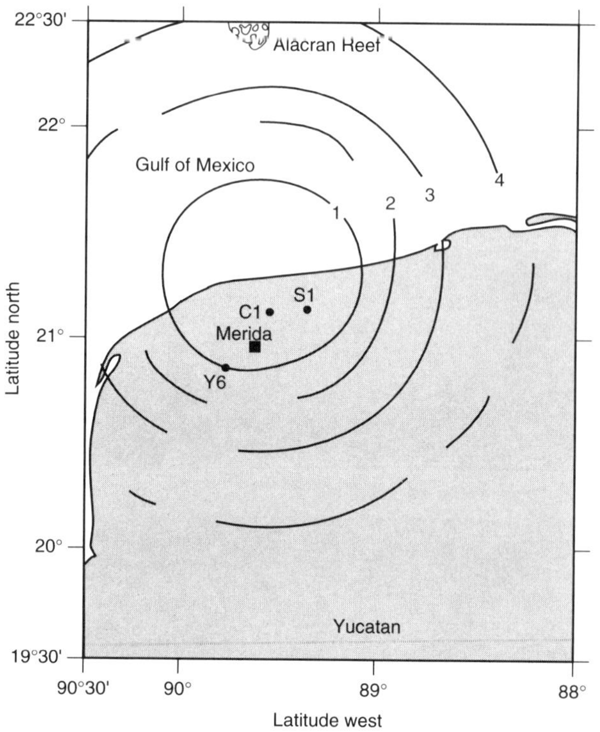

FIGURE 11–3 The subsurface geology evidence revealed the presence of a meteorite crater first from a deep well drilled at Chicxulub on the Yucatan peninsula in Mexico. Drilling at sites C1 (Chicxulub), S1, and Y6 has revealed features typical of a meteorite impact, such as impact melt rocks and shattered rocks (called "breccias"). The dimensions of the crater rings, from geophysical studies, and the age, based on the radioactive dating of the impacted rocks, make the Chicxulub crater a likely candidate for the great impact at the Cretaceous–Tertiary boundary. (Reprinted with permission from V. L. Sharpton, K. Burke et al., 1993, *Science,* v. 261, p. 1564. Copyright American Association for the Advancement of Science.)

transmitted through the atmosphere. The possible effects fall into four categories:

1. The impact could blow dust, water, and gases into the stratosphere. The fine-grained materials could remain in the stratosphere for several months, resulting in a darkening of Earth's surface. The resulting cooling and the attenuated light would strongly affect the life forms which had adjusted to a warm climate prevalent at that time from pole to pole. The surface temperature of the planet in the Cretaceous could have been 15°C warmer than it is today. A sudden chilling would have

taken a heavy toll on the organisms unable to adjust to the new conditions. Animals that could retreat to burrows or lakes or streams would be less affected by the drop in temperature than animals living exposed at the surface. Plants would die and, while seeds would persist, the primary food supply would be diminished. The food chain at the ocean surface as well as on the land surface would be broken and presumably affect the survival of species in that chain. Most would die out, leaving a few species as survivors. Organisms of the ocean depths would be less affected—depending on stored organic matter from better times for food and not subject to large temperature changes. This scenario was an extension of thoughts about large volcanic eruptions and their influence on climate. It also provided a strong impetus to the "nuclear winter" hypothesis.

2. The impactor was a comet and the carbon compounds in the comet were transformed to hydrogen cyanide gas which asphyxiated life at the surface. Animals living in relative isolation from the rapidly changing atmosphere would survive until the hydrogen cyanide was destroyed by reactions in the atmosphere. The survivors would be the same ones cited in the first option.

3. Another option is the release of massive amounts of carbon dioxide to the atmosphere as the result of the thermal decomposition of limestone at the site of impact. The addition of large amounts of carbon dioxide would raise the temperature of the atmosphere almost immediately with the increase of greenhouse warming (see Chapter 3). The planetary surface and the ocean surface layer would be hot enough to cause major discomfort to the organisms living there. Again, relief would come to those organisms protected from the intense heat, such as burrowers and deep-ocean dwellers.

   Any large amount of carbon dioxide in the atmosphere, from whatever source, will also act as a lethal narcotic as seen in the local devastation from the carbon dioxide gas bubble release at Lake Nyos in Cameroon in August 1984.

4. Other effects may also contribute to marked short-term changes in the environment. Examples include the formation of acid rain on a grand scale and global wildfires. The acid rain is a consequence mainly of the formation of nitric oxides from atmospheric nitrogen and oxygen as a result of the energy impact. It is similar to that produced in power plants and internal combustion engines at present—except on a massive global scale. This acidification might influence the terrestrial flora and

> thus the fauna and in the uppermost layers of the ocean the increased acid addition will lower the pH (increase the acidity) even though the oceans are basic and strongly buffered as a whole. Also, the nitric oxide gases could act to destroy Earth's ozone shield prior to forming nitric acid rain. This process would increase the ultraviolet flux if all else remained the same and thereby threaten the exposed fauna and flora. Evidence for global wildfires is found in specific organic compounds associated with the Cretaceous–Tertiary boundary clays virtually at every site. These compounds are formed uniquely by the burning of terrestrial biomass. How such a global conflagration could occur remains a mystery, as we only have an understanding of regional fire effects such as those produced by the great Yellowstone Park fire of 1990. The effects of such large fires, commonly set by lightning, can be seen in sedimentary records in lake sediments and marine deposits, but the environmental impact is local and fairly small. Most likely, changes in atmospheric conditions caused by the impact resulted in global lightning discharges and ignited the biomass everywhere. Massive burning of much of the world's biomass in a short time scale would be required to yield the inferred quantities of characteristic organic compounds of fire origin found in the clays at the Cretaceous–Tertiary boundary everywhere.

Whatever the cause or combination of causes may have been to alter the environment, the argument is made that they were, separately or together, powerful enough to cause massive destruction of species. Those species that were protected by their habitats or resilient under changing environmental conditions survived. The survivors inherited Earth and proceeded to adapt by the process of natural selection to all the ecological niches available to them. The Cenozoic was a time of extensive "experimentation" with an open and slowly changing environment. The extraordinary Cenozoic diversity of species both on land and sea indicates that a global catastrophe is accommodated by survivors who are then capable of exploiting every vacated ecological niche.

THE PALEOZOIC–MESOZOIC (PERMIAN–TRIASSIC) BOUNDARY EXTINCTIONS

The extinctions that occurred at the Permian–Triassic boundary were greater in number than at the Cretaceous–Tertiary boundary. Up to 96% of all marine invertebrate species present at the end of the Permian were obliterated, and of the ninety genera of reptiles (who had just appeared on the evolutionary scene) only one remained after the extinctions at the Permian–Triassic boundary. There is no evidence of a major cosmic impact event at that boundary to explain the changes, as was possible at the Cretaceous–Tertiary boundary.

The end of the Permian saw the formation of the one global land mass called Pangaea (Chapter 1). Because of this event sea level fell at the Permian–Triassic boundary and the ice ages of the late Paleozoic Era came to a halt. The geography of a single land mass meant that major parts were isolated from the oceans and deprived of moisture. The Triassic Period is noted for deposits that are indicative of this aridity. It has been argued that this unique geography would have affected life patterns so that extinctions and innovations occurred in a number of habitats.

The Permian–Triassic boundary was also a time of one of the largest outpourings of basaltic lava on the continent in a broad area we now identify as northeastern Asia. It has been suggested that the release of huge quantities of volatile sulfur compounds to the stratosphere, under conditions of strong convective cell formation in the atmosphere resulting from the intense heat of the large lava field, had a strong cooling effect on the planet. The formation of sulfate aerosols in the stratosphere would be comparable in its effects to the meteorite impact effects discussed above except that volatile sulfur compounds would be the unique active agent of environmental change at the Permian–Triassic boundary.

FUTURE CATASTROPHES

The meteorite impact of 65 million years ago (the Cretaceous–Tertiary boundary) has been the largest that has been well documented from the geologic record. Meteorite craters of a variety of ages have been observed in the rocks. Some are features easily identified by surficial expressions such as Meteor Crater in Arizona (Fig. 11–1). Others have been found by aerial surveys and satellite imaging. Still others have been found by drilling for oil or water or by gravity and seismic profiling (Fig. 11–3). Over 100 craters on Earth have been observed by these methods. They have been determined to represent impacts of various ages ranging over a billion years or so. The largest one found so far, in Ontario, Canada, is 124 miles (200 km) in diameter and is 1.6 billion years old.

Obviously Earth, as well as the other planets, is subject to pummeling by asteroids and comets. The question to ask is how frequently such encounters will occur and, more specifically, what is the likelihood that an impact of the size at the Cretaceous–Tertiary boundary might occur again in the near future.

Astronomers have calculated that there are presently at least 400 Earth-crossing asteroids two kilometers or more in diameter. If one of these should hit Earth, the environmental effects would resemble those at the Cretaceous–Tertiary boundary. The frequency of such a collision is one in about a million years. Some scientists argue that tracking asteroids would give a chance in the future to intercept and destroy the largest of the incoming projectiles. A current assessment of observed asteroid orbits, however, shows no prospect of a collision at least through the twenty-first century. On probability arguments, however, it has been estimated that there is one chance in 10,000 that an impact of a 2-km diameter body could occur. If that should happen it would result in massive death for humans and living things in general.

We may not be waiting for the next meteorite impact to effect changes in the species make-up of Earth. Humans have been successful in altering the biological landscape since their occupation of Earth. The elimination of species by hunting, displacement, or neglect has proceeded since the advent of organized human activity. The decrease in biodiversity is in itself a catastrophe-like event, although extinctions and displacements have been local rather than global.

EPILOGUE

Earth's environment is always changing. That is the hallmark of our planet. We have some idea of the range of changes in surface temperature, atmospheric composition, geography, and biology from records in sediments, rocks, and ice caps as well as historical records. The courses of these changes are being understood better each day, but our knowledge is so far from complete that we cannot easily make accurate forecasts into the future about changes that might occur.

Added to what we recognize as natural changes, humans have added their own characteristic effects. Migration and the exploitation of the land and sea for resources have seriously affected the nature of the land and the diversity of life. The growing population of the world has accelerated these changes. The water-retentive qualities of the land have changed due to deforestation, streams have been drained virtually to dryness because of agricultural needs, and erosion of soil by wind and water has greatly increased. Perhaps the least significant effects, surprisingly, are those due to the addition of carbon dioxide and other greenhouse gases to the atmosphere!

The growth of the population, coupled with changes in the environmental effects of water and land use, has exacerbated what appears to be a tribally driven propensity toward conflict and even mutual annihilation. More people die each year from wars and massacres than projected from the effects of depleted ozone or increased carbon dioxide.

It is a strange juxtaposition of celebrations—Earth Day and Earth Week in April occur within the same week that we set aside to remember the

Holocaust of World War II in which six million Jews were killed. It is also the week to remember the first holocaust of this century in World War I, in which one million Armenians were killed in an act we now call genocide. Aggressive or dying empires are not the only agents of human destruction. Greed, tribal feuds, and international manipulations have led to massive programmed destructions of large populations.

Our capacity as a species for self-destruction by direct killing far transcends our ability to do it by the subtle procedure of altering the environment. Yet human behavior may deteriorate faster because of changes in the environment and the explosive growth of the population of the world.

The limiting environmental property for the survival of humans is the availability of water suitable for drinking and for the growth of crops. The quality of drinking water is deteriorating in many places and the amount of water available for crop growth with the present distribution system is diminishing. Crop growth, if enough water were available, could supply the population of the world with plenty of food. Yet if the population increases faster than the rate of controlling the water supply, there can only be the disaster of global overpopulation, with the consequences of massive starvation and mass killing that we see in many parts of the world today.

Yet ample water has its price. The delivery of water to those parts of the world needing it requires heroic programs of water transport and desalination. All cures to our water problems are energy intensive. If we are cautious about accelerating the use of fossil fuels, then other energy sources must be sought. Although nuclear energy makes up about 10 to 20% of the present energy "mix," increased use must be accompanied by a well-developed plan for disposal of radioactive waste. Perhaps the greatest caution in the proliferation of nuclear reactors throughout the world is the growing risk of the spread of nuclear technology and fissionable materials to nations who have no compunctions about making and using nuclear weapons in warfare or terrorism.

The solar option remains viable. Solar cells and wind power are feasible as long as the methods of transfer of the energy from the special regional points of generation to where it is needed can be worked out—a non-trivial undertaking.

The Biblical command to Adam and Eve to "subdue the Earth" is often interpreted as "exploit Earth, incautiously." A more likely interpretation is "to understand Earth and act wisely." Our capacity to change Earth's environment even more than we have already done is undoubted. A scientific understanding of Earth and the wisdom to use this knowledge will help in properly "subduing Earth" rather than making it a shambles. Along the way we had also better learn to get along with each other or Earth will be a shambles no matter how sensitive we are to its environmental health.

INDEX